Insight Journal

A One-Year Journal

Day: _____ Date: ____ / ____ / ____

*What are two things you hope to achieve
during the coming year, and why?*

_____

_____

_____

_____

_____

_____

_____

_____

_____

*What was a notable or "aha" moment from today,
and why?*

_____

_____

_____

_____

_____

_____

_____

_____

⭐

Day: _____ Date: ____ / ____ / ____

*In what two ways are you living an authentic
life?*

_____

_____

_____

_____

_____

_____

_____

_____

_____

_____

*What was a notable or "aha" moment from today,
and why?*

_____

_____

_____

_____

_____

_____

_____

_____

_____

_____

✫

Day: _____ Date: ___ / ___ / ___

*What was the last thing you criticized
yourself for, and why?*

_____

_____

_____

_____

_____

_____

_____

_____

_____

_____

*What was a notable or "aha" moment from today,
and why?*

_____

_____

_____

_____

_____

_____

_____

_____

_____

_____

★

Day: _____ Date: ____ / ____ / ____

*What was the last challenge you faced, and
how did you handle it?*

_____

_____

_____

_____

_____

_____

_____

_____

_____

*What was a notable or "aha" moment from today,
and why?*

_____

_____

_____

_____

_____

_____

_____

_____

_____

★

Day: _____ Date: ___ / ___ / ___

What have you noticed about your
boundaries lately?

_____

_____

_____

_____

_____

_____

_____

_____

_____

_____

What was a notable or "aha" moment from today,
and why?

_____

_____

_____

_____

_____

_____

_____

_____

_____

_____

★

Day: _____ Date: ____ / ____ / ____

*In what two ways have your expressed your
individuality lately?*

_____

_____

_____

_____

_____

_____

_____

_____

_____

*What was a notable or "aha" moment from today,
and why?*

_____

_____

_____

_____

_____

_____

_____

_____

_____

✯

What you say yes to is just as important as what you say no to. You only have so much time and energy, and it's important to value both.

Day: _____ Date:____ / ____ / ____

What are a few of the more notable moments from the past week, and in what ways (if any) will this change how you approach things moving forward?

_____

_____

_____

_____

_____

_____

_____

_____

_____

_____

_____

_____

_____

_____

_____

_____

_____

_____

✫

Day: _____ Date: ____ / ____ / ____

*What is your favorite thing to do during your
leisure time lately, and why?*

_____

_____

_____

_____

_____

_____

_____

_____

_____

*What was a notable or "aha" moment from today,
and why?*

_____

_____

_____

_____

_____

_____

_____

_____

_____

★

Day: _____ Date: ____ / ____ / ____

*What is the last thing you read, and what did
you take away from it?*

_____

_____

_____

_____

_____

_____

_____

_____

_____

_____

*What was a notable or "aha" moment from today,
and why?*

_____

_____

_____

_____

_____

_____

_____

_____

_____

★

Day: _____ Date: ____ / ____ / ____

What are you feeling grateful for today, and why?

_____

_____

_____

_____

_____

_____

_____

_____

_____

_____

What was a notable or "aha" moment from today, and why?

_____

_____

_____

_____

_____

_____

_____

_____

_____

_____

★

Day: _____ Date: ____ / ____ / ____

What new place have you been to lately? What did you learn about yourself while you were there?

_____

_____

_____

_____

_____

_____

_____

_____

_____

What was a notable or "aha" moment from today, and why?

_____

_____

_____

_____

_____

_____

_____

_____

_____

★

Day: _____ Date: ____ / ____ / ____

What has been your biggest accomplishment
lately, and why?

_____

_____

_____

_____

_____

_____

_____

_____

_____

What was a notable or "aha" moment from today,
and why?

_____

_____

_____

_____

_____

_____

_____

_____

_____

★

Day: _____ Date: ____ / ____ / ____

What have you been most afraid of doing (or
trying) lately, and why?

_____

_____

_____

_____

_____

_____

_____

_____

_____

_____

What was a notable or "aha" moment from today,
and why?

_____

_____

_____

_____

_____

_____

_____

_____

_____

_____

★

Day: _____ Date: ____/ ____ /____

What are a few of the more notable moments from the
past week, and in what ways (if any) will this change
how you approach things moving forward?

_____

_____

_____

_____

_____

_____

_____

_____

_____

_____

_____

_____

_____

_____

_____

_____

_____

_____

_____

⭐

Day: _____ Date: ___ / ___ / ___

If you really valued yourself, what is one thing
you'd do differently in your life, and why?

_____

_____

_____

_____

_____

_____

_____

_____

_____

_____

What was a notable or "aha" moment from today,
and why?

_____

_____

_____

_____

_____

_____

_____

_____

_____

★

Day: _____ Date: ___ / ___ / ___

When did you last spend time with a friend?
Who were you with, and what did you do?

_____

_____

_____

_____

_____

_____

_____

_____

_____

_____

What was a notable or "aha" moment from today,
and why?

_____

_____

_____

_____

_____

_____

_____

_____

_____

_____

★

Day: _____ Date: ____ / ____ / ____

When was the last time you felt really "alive?"
What about the experience made you feel this way?

_____

_____

_____

_____

_____

_____

_____

_____

_____

What was a notable or "aha" moment from today,
and why?

_____

_____

_____

_____

_____

_____

_____

_____

_____

★

Day: _____ Date: ____ / ____ / ____

*Do you have a purpose, and if so, what is it, and
when was the last time you felt it pulling at you?*

_____

_____

_____

_____

_____

_____

_____

_____

_____

*What was a notable or "aha" moment from today,
and why?*

_____

_____

_____

_____

_____

_____

_____

_____

★

Day: _____ Date: ____ / ____ / ____

*What is the most recent painful thing to
happen in your life?*

_____

_____

_____

_____

_____

_____

_____

_____

_____

*What was a notable or "aha" moment from today,
and why?*

_____

_____

_____

_____

_____

_____

_____

_____

_____

★

An "aha" moment is so much more than a moment, it's a delicious flash of clarity where the Divine decides to share a secret with us.

Day: _____ Date: ____ / ____ / ____

What is the healthiest (or unhealthiest) relationship you have in your life right now, and what makes it this way?

_____

_____

_____

_____

_____

_____

_____

_____

_____

_____

What was a notable or "aha" moment from today, and why?

_____

_____

_____

_____

_____

_____

_____

_____

_____

_____

★

Day: _____ Date: ____ / ____ / ____

*What are a few of the more notable moments from the
past week, and in what ways (if any) will this change
how you approach things moving forward?*

_____

_____

_____

_____

_____

_____

_____

_____

_____

_____

_____

_____

_____

_____

_____

_____

_____

_____

_____

✫

Day: _____ Date: ____ / ____ / ____

*If someone were to observe your actions from the past month,
what would they think you really care about, and why?*

_____

_____

_____

_____

_____

_____

_____

_____

_____

_____

*What was a notable or "aha" moment from today,
and why?*

_____

_____

_____

_____

_____

_____

_____

_____

_____

_____

✯

Day: _____ Date: ____ / ____ / ____

*What would you like to change about
yourself, and why?*

_____

_____

_____

_____

_____

_____

_____

_____

_____

*What was a notable or "aha" moment from today,
and why?*

_____

_____

_____

_____

_____

_____

_____

_____

★

Day: _____ Date: ____ / ____ / ____

Is there something that you talk about doing,
but never follow through on? If so, why?

_____

_____

_____

_____

_____

_____

_____

_____

_____

_____

What was a notable or "aha" moment from today,
and why?

_____

_____

_____

_____

_____

_____

_____

_____

_____

_____

★

Day: _____ Date: ____ / ____ / ____

What is one aspect of your character or
personality that you like, and why?

_____

_____

_____

_____

_____

_____

_____

_____

_____

What was a notable or "aha" moment from today,
and why?

_____

_____

_____

_____

_____

_____

_____

_____

_____

★

Day: _____ Date: ____ / ____ / ____

What has been your favorite way to spend
your free time lately, and why?

_____

_____

_____

_____

_____

_____

_____

_____

_____

_____

What was a notable or "aha" moment from today,
and why?

_____

_____

_____

_____

_____

_____

_____

_____

_____

★

Day: _____ Date: ___ / ___ / ___

What is the last goal you achieved, and did
you celebrate it?

_____

_____

_____

_____

_____

_____

_____

_____

_____

_____

What was a notable or "aha" moment from today,
and why?

_____

_____

_____

_____

_____

_____

_____

_____

_____

_____

★

All of your victories
are worth celebrating.

Day: _____ Date: ___/___/___

What are a few of the more notable moments from the past week, and in what ways (if any) will this change how you approach things moving forward?

_____

_____

_____

_____

_____

_____

_____

_____

_____

_____

_____

_____

_____

_____

_____

_____

_____

_____

_____

★

Day: _____ Date: ____ / ____ / ____

What two words would you use to describe
yourself, and why?

_____

_____

_____

_____

_____

_____

_____

_____

_____

What was a notable or "aha" moment from today,
and why?

_____

_____

_____

_____

_____

_____

_____

_____

_____

★

Day: _____ Date: ____ / ____ / ____

What important realization have you had about yourself
lately, and how has this realization changed you?

_____

_____

_____

_____

_____

_____

_____

_____

_____

_____

What was a notable or "aha" moment from today,
and why?

_____

_____

_____

_____

_____

_____

_____

_____

_____

★

Day: _____ Date: ____ / ____ / ____

*In what two ways have you treated yourself
with value today?*

_____

_____

_____

_____

_____

_____

_____

_____

_____

*What was a notable or "aha" moment from today,
and why?*

_____

_____

_____

_____

_____

_____

_____

_____

_____

★

Day: _____ Date: ____ / ____ / ____

*What two things are you hoping to achieve
during the coming month, and why?*

_____

_____

_____

_____

_____

_____

_____

_____

_____

_____

*What was a notable or "aha" moment from today,
and why?*

_____

_____

_____

_____

_____

_____

_____

_____

_____

_____

★

Day: _____ Date: ____ / ____ / ____

What was the last lesson you learned the hard way?

_____

_____

_____

_____

_____

_____

_____

_____

_____

What was a notable or "aha" moment from today, and why?

_____

_____

_____

_____

_____

_____

_____

_____

_____

_____

✮

Day: _____ Date: ____ / ____ / ____

*What are two traits in people that make you either
comfortable or uncomfortable, and why?*

_____

_____

_____

_____

_____

_____

_____

_____

_____

_____

*What was a notable or "aha" moment from today,
and why?*

_____

_____

_____

_____

_____

_____

_____

_____

_____

★

Day: _____ Date: ____ / ____ / ____

What are a few of the more notable moments from the past week, and in what ways (if any) will this change how you approach things moving forward?

_____

_____

_____

_____

_____

_____

_____

_____

_____

_____

_____

_____

_____

_____

_____

_____

_____

_____

_____

Day: _____ Date: ____ / ____ / ____

What is one positive (or negative) belief you have about what's possible in your life, and where did this belief originate?

_____

_____

_____

_____

_____

_____

_____

_____

_____

What was a notable or "aha" moment from today, and why?

_____

_____

_____

_____

_____

_____

_____

_____

_____

★

Day: _____ Date: ____ / ____ / ____

What was the last unhealthy situation you left, and what made you realize you needed to leave?

_____

_____

_____

_____

_____

_____

_____

_____

_____

_____

What was a notable or "aha" moment from today, and why?

_____

_____

_____

_____

_____

_____

_____

_____

_____

★

Day: _____ Date: ___ / ___ / ___

If you could go back in time, what advice would you give your younger self, and why?

_____

_____

_____

_____

_____

_____

_____

_____

_____

_____

What was a notable or "aha" moment from today, and why?

_____

_____

_____

_____

_____

_____

_____

_____

_____

★

Day: _____ Date: ____ / ____ / ____

What new habit (if any) would you like to
cultivate, and why?

_____

_____

_____

_____

_____

_____

_____

_____

_____

_____

What was a notable or "aha" moment from today,
and why?

_____

_____

_____

_____

_____

_____

_____

_____

_____

⭐

Day: _____ Date: ____ / ____ / ____

In what two ways are you different this year from
how you were around this time last year?

_____

_____

_____

_____

_____

_____

_____

_____

_____

What was a notable or "aha" moment from today,
and why?

_____

_____

_____

_____

_____

_____

_____

_____

_____

★

Day: _____ Date: ____ / ____ / ____

What have you worried about the most lately, and why?

_____

_____

_____

_____

_____

_____

_____

_____

_____

_____

What was a notable or "aha" moment from today, and why?

_____

_____

_____

_____

_____

_____

_____

_____

_____

★

Day: _____ Date: ____ / ____ / ____

*What are a few of the more notable moments from the
past week, and in what ways (if any) will this change
how you approach things moving forward?*

_____

_____

_____

_____

_____

_____

_____

_____

_____

_____

_____

_____

_____

_____

_____

_____

_____

_____

_____

★

Day: _____ Date: ____ / ____ / ____

In what way have you been courageous lately, and why?

_____

_____

_____

_____

_____

_____

_____

_____

_____

_____

What was a notable or "aha" moment from today, and why?

_____

_____

_____

_____

_____

_____

_____

_____

_____

★

Day: _____ Date: ___ / ___ / ___

*What is one small change you could make to your
daily routine to enjoy your life more?*

_____

_____

_____

_____

_____

_____

_____

_____

_____

_____

*What was a notable or "aha" moment from today,
and why?*

_____

_____

_____

_____

_____

_____

_____

_____

_____

_____

✮

Day: _____ Date: ____ / ____ / ____

How are you feeling right now, and why?

_____

_____

_____

_____

_____

_____

_____

_____

_____

What was a notable or "aha" moment from today,
and why?

_____

_____

_____

_____

_____

_____

_____

_____

_____

★

Day: _____ Date: ____ / ____ / ____

What has been a motivating force for you lately,
and why?

_____

_____

_____

_____

_____

_____

_____

_____

_____

_____

What was a notable or "aha" moment from today,
and why?

_____

_____

_____

_____

_____

_____

_____

_____

_____

_____

★

There is a small voice inside you that is always trying to get your attention. It's the voice of your highest and best self, and it has a never-ending series of important messages for you.

Day: _____ Date: ____ / ____ / ____

What is a bad (or good) habit you have, and what purpose is this habit serving?

_____

_____

_____

_____

_____

_____

_____

_____

_____

_____

What was a notable or "aha" moment from today, and why?

_____

_____

_____

_____

_____

_____

_____

_____

_____

_____

★

Day: _____ Date: ____ / ____ / ____

*What is one way you could bring more peace into
your life?*

_____

_____

_____

_____

_____

_____

_____

_____

_____

_____

*What was a notable or "aha" moment from today,
and why?*

_____

_____

_____

_____

_____

_____

_____

_____

_____

_____

✫

Day: _____ Date: ____ / ____ / ____

What are a few of the more notable moments from the past week, and in what ways (if any) will this change how you approach things moving forward?

_____

_____

_____

_____

_____

_____

_____

_____

_____

_____

_____

_____

_____

_____

_____

_____

_____

_____

_____

_____

_____

_____

⭐

Day: _____ Date: ____ / ____ / ____

*Who is the person you've spent the most time with
lately, and what kind of influence have they had on you?*

_____

_____

_____

_____

_____

_____

_____

_____

_____

*What was a notable or "aha" moment from today,
and why?*

_____

_____

_____

_____

_____

_____

_____

_____

_____

★

Day: _____ Date: ___ / ___ / ___

What was the high point of your day today, and why?

_____

_____

_____

_____

_____

_____

_____

_____

_____

What was a notable or "aha" moment from today, and why?

_____

_____

_____

_____

_____

_____

_____

_____

_____

★

Day: _____ Date: ____ / ____ / ____

What has been a deal breaker lately when it
comes to how you are treated, and why?

_____

_____

_____

_____

_____

_____

_____

_____

_____

_____

What was a notable or "aha" moment from today,
and why?

_____

_____

_____

_____

_____

_____

_____

_____

_____

_____

✫

Day: _____ Date: ____ / ____ / ____

What is a strength you are glad to have,
and why?

_____

_____

_____

_____

_____

_____

_____

_____

_____

What was a notable or "aha" moment from today,
and why?

_____

_____

_____

_____

_____

_____

_____

_____

_____

★

Day: _____ Date: ____ / ____ / ____

Who has been the most inspiring person you've come across lately, and why?

_____

_____

_____

_____

_____

_____

_____

_____

_____

What was a notable or "aha" moment from today, and why?

_____

_____

_____

_____

_____

_____

_____

_____

_____

★

Day: _____ Date: ____ / ____ / ____

*What is one thing you would like to have, be, or
do in the future, and why?*

_____

_____

_____

_____

_____

_____

_____

_____

_____

*What was a notable or "aha" moment from today,
and why?*

_____

_____

_____

_____

_____

_____

_____

_____

_____

★

Day: ———————————— Date:——— / ——— / ———

What are a few of the more notable moments from the past week, and in what ways (if any) will this change how you approach things moving forward?

_____

_____

_____

_____

_____

_____

_____

_____

_____

_____

_____

_____

_____

_____

_____

_____

_____

_____

_____

★

Day: _____ Date: ____ / ____ / ____

What do you need a break from,
and why?

_____

_____

_____

_____

_____

_____

_____

_____

_____

What was a notable or "aha" moment from today,
and why?

_____

_____

_____

_____

_____

_____

_____

_____

_____

★

Life is journey, not a race. It's okay to rest.

Day: _____ Date: ____ / ____ / ____

In what ways is your external environment a reflection of your internal environment, and why do you think this is?

_____

_____

_____

_____

_____

_____

_____

_____

_____

_____

What was a notable or "aha" moment from today, and why?

_____

_____

_____

_____

_____

_____

_____

_____

_____

★

Day: _____ Date: ____ / ____ / ____

What do you feel you "must do" in this life, and why?

_____

_____

_____

_____

_____

_____

_____

_____

_____

_____

What was a notable or "aha" moment from today, and why?

_____

_____

_____

_____

_____

_____

_____

_____

_____

_____

★

Day: _____ Date: ____ / ____ / ____

What was the last big obstacle you overcame, and how did you do it?

_____

_____

_____

_____

_____

_____

_____

_____

_____

What was a notable or "aha" moment from today, and why?

_____

_____

_____

_____

_____

_____

_____

_____

_____

★

Day: _____ Date: ____ / ____ / ____

*What are two things you hope to achieve during
the coming month, and why?*

_____

_____

_____

_____

_____

_____

_____

_____

_____

*What was a notable or "aha" moment from today,
and why?*

_____

_____

_____

_____

_____

_____

_____

_____

_____

★

Day: _____ Date: ____ / ____ / ____

What was the last thing you did out of obligation,
fear, or guilt, and why?

_____

_____

_____

_____

_____

_____

_____

_____

_____

_____

What was a notable or "aha" moment from today,
and why?

_____

_____

_____

_____

_____

_____

_____

_____

_____

★

Day: _____ Date: ____ / ____ / ____

*What is the best quote you've heard lately, and
why do you like it?*

_____

_____

_____

_____

_____

_____

_____

_____

_____

_____

*What was a notable or "aha" moment from today,
and why?*

_____

_____

_____

_____

_____

_____

_____

_____

_____

★

Day: _____ Date: ____ / ____ / ____

What are a few of the more notable moments from the past week, and in what ways (if any) will this change how you approach things moving forward?

_____

_____

_____

_____

_____

_____

_____

_____

_____

_____

_____

_____

_____

_____

_____

_____

_____

_____

_____

★

Day: _____ Date: ____ / ____ / ____

*How have you handled the stress in your life
lately?*

_____

_____

_____

_____

_____

_____

_____

_____

_____

*What was a notable or "aha" moment from today,
and why?*

_____

_____

_____

_____

_____

_____

_____

_____

_____

★

Stress isn't necessarily a bad thing. It's generally a signal that we need to do things differently—and a sign that it's time for us to grow.

Day: _____ Date: ____ / ____ / ____

How are you feeling right now,
and why?

_____

_____

_____

_____

_____

_____

_____

_____

_____

What was a notable or "aha" moment from today,
and why?

_____

_____

_____

_____

_____

_____

_____

_____

_____

★

Day: _____ Date: ____ / ____ / ____

*What is one way that "public" you has differed
from "private" you lately, and why?*

_____

_____

_____

_____

_____

_____

_____

_____

_____

_____

*What was a notable or "aha" moment from today,
and why?*

_____

_____

_____

_____

_____

_____

_____

_____

_____

★

Day: _____ Date: ____ / ____ / ____

When was the last time you did something fun?
What did you do?

_____

_____

_____

_____

_____

_____

_____

_____

_____

What was a notable or "aha" moment from today,
and why?

_____

_____

_____

_____

_____

_____

_____

_____

_____

★

Day: _____ Date: ____ / ____ / ____

In what way have you grown as a person lately,
and what sparked that growth?

_____

_____

_____

_____

_____

_____

_____

_____

_____

_____

What was a notable or "aha" moment from today,
and why?

_____

_____

_____

_____

_____

_____

_____

_____

_____

_____

★

Day: _____ Date: ____ / ____ / ____

What is one area of your life you'd like to change,
and why?

_____

_____

_____

_____

_____

_____

_____

_____

_____

_____

What was a notable or "aha" moment from today,
and why?

_____

_____

_____

_____

_____

_____

_____

_____

_____

★

Day: _____ Date: ____ / ____ / ____

What are a few of the more notable moments from the past week, and in what ways (if any) will this change how you approach things moving forward?

_____

_____

_____

_____

_____

_____

_____

_____

_____

_____

_____

_____

_____

_____

_____

_____

_____

_____

_____

✦

An authentic life is one where you are living a life of purpose on purpose.

Day: _____ Date: ___ / ___ / ___

In what ways have you lived an authentic life
lately?

_____

_____

_____

_____

_____

_____

_____

_____

_____

_____

What was a notable or "aha" moment from today,
and why?

_____

_____

_____

_____

_____

_____

_____

_____

_____

✶

Day: _____ Date: ____ / ____ / ____

Who is your biggest supporter, and how do they
best show their support?

_____

_____

_____

_____

_____

_____

_____

_____

_____

_____

What was a notable or "aha" moment from today,
and why?

_____

_____

_____

_____

_____

_____

_____

_____

_____

★

Day: _____ Date: ____ / ____ / ____

Who do you enjoy being around,
and why?

_____

_____

_____

_____

_____

_____

_____

_____

_____

What was a notable or "aha" moment from today,
and why?

_____

_____

_____

_____

_____

_____

_____

_____

_____

★

Day: _____ Date: ____ / ____ / ____

*What is one thing you admire about the last
person you spent quality time with, and why?*

_____

_____

_____

_____

_____

_____

_____

_____

_____

_____

*What was a notable or "aha" moment from today,
and why?*

_____

_____

_____

_____

_____

_____

_____

_____

_____

★

Day: _____ Date: ____ / ____ / ____

What is the last big change you made, and how do you feel about it?

_____

_____

_____

_____

_____

_____

_____

_____

_____

_____

What was a notable or "aha" moment from today, and why?

_____

_____

_____

_____

_____

_____

_____

_____

_____

★

Day: _____ Date: ____ / ____ / ____

*What is the best movie you've seen this year (or in
general) and what about it resonated with you?*

_____

_____

_____

_____

_____

_____

_____

_____

_____

*What was a notable or "aha" moment from today,
and why?*

_____

_____

_____

_____

_____

_____

_____

_____

_____

★

Day: _____ Date: ____ / ____ / ____

What are a few of the more notable moments from the past week, and in what ways (if any) will this change how you approach things moving forward?

_____

_____

_____

_____

_____

_____

_____

_____

_____

_____

_____

_____

_____

_____

_____

_____

_____

_____

★

Day: _____ Date: ____ / ____ / ____

*What are some of the positive (or negative) things
you tell yourself, and why?*

_____

_____

_____

_____

_____

_____

_____

_____

_____

_____

*What was a notable or "aha" moment from today,
and why?*

_____

_____

_____

_____

_____

_____

_____

_____

_____

★

Talk to yourself like you would a good friend.

Day: _____ Date: ____ / ____ / ____

What is the last book (or article, blog post, etc.)
you read? What did you take away from it?

_____

_____

_____

_____

_____

_____

_____

_____

_____

What was a notable or "aha" moment from today,
and why?

_____

_____

_____

_____

_____

_____

_____

_____

_____

★

Day: _____ Date: ___ / ___ / ___

What (or who) do you tend to make excuses for,
and why?

_____

_____

_____

_____

_____

_____

_____

_____

_____

What was a notable or "aha" moment from today,
and why?

_____

_____

_____

_____

_____

_____

_____

_____

_____

⭐

Day: _____ Date: ____ / ____ / ____

*What do you need to do to take care of yourself
today, and why?*

_____

_____

_____

_____

_____

_____

_____

_____

_____

*What was a notable or "aha" moment from today,
and why?*

_____

_____

_____

_____

_____

_____

_____

_____

★

Day: _____ Date: ____ / ____ / ____

What has been the best use of your time lately,
and why?

_____

_____

_____

_____

_____

_____

_____

_____

_____

What was a notable or "aha" moment from today,
and why?

_____

_____

_____

_____

_____

_____

_____

_____

_____

★

Day: _____ Date: ____ / ____ / ____

*What was the high (or low) point of your day
today, and why?*

_____

_____

_____

_____

_____

_____

_____

_____

_____

_____

*What was a notable or "aha" moment from today,
and why?*

_____

_____

_____

_____

_____

_____

_____

_____

_____

★

Self-care isn't a luxury, it's a necessity.

Day: _____ Date:____ / ____ / ____

What are a few of the more notable moments from the past week, and in what ways (if any) will this change how you approach things moving forward?

_____

_____

_____

_____

_____

_____

_____

_____

_____

_____

_____

_____

_____

_____

_____

_____

_____

_____

_____

★

Day: _____ Date: ____ / ____ / ____

What is your dream job,
and why?

_____

_____

_____

_____

_____

_____

_____

_____

_____

What was a notable or "aha" moment from today,
and why?

_____

_____

_____

_____

_____

_____

_____

_____

_____

★

Day: _____ Date: ___ / ___ / ___

When was the last time you got angry? What
happened, and how did you calm yourself down?

_____

_____

_____

_____

_____

_____

_____

_____

_____

What was a notable or "aha" moment from today,
and why?

_____

_____

_____

_____

_____

_____

_____

_____

_____

★

Day: _____ Date: ____ / ____ / ____

*What is your most significant memory from this
year so far, and why?*

_____

_____

_____

_____

_____

_____

_____

_____

_____

_____

*What was a notable or "aha" moment from today,
and why?*

_____

_____

_____

_____

_____

_____

_____

_____

_____

★

Day: _____ Date: ____ / ____ / ____

How are you feeling right now,
and why?

_____

_____

_____

_____

_____

_____

_____

_____

_____

_____

What was a notable or "aha" moment from today,
and why?

_____

_____

_____

_____

_____

_____

_____

_____

_____

★

Having problems isn't the problem; it's how we cope with our problems that tends to be the problem.

Day: _____ Date: ____ / ____ / ____

What has been your favorite website lately,
and why?

_____

_____

_____

_____

_____

_____

_____

_____

_____

What was a notable or "aha" moment from today,
and why?

_____

_____

_____

_____

_____

_____

_____

_____

_____

★

Day: _____ Date: ____ / ____ / ____

What is the last caring/considerate thing you did
for someone, and why?

_____

_____

_____

_____

_____

_____

_____

_____

_____

What was a notable or "aha" moment from today,
and why?

_____

_____

_____

_____

_____

_____

_____

_____

_____

★

Day: _____ Date: ____ / ____ / ____

*What are two things you hope to achieve during
the coming month, and why?*

_____

_____

_____

_____

_____

_____

_____

_____

_____

_____

*What was a notable or "aha" moment from today,
and why?*

_____

_____

_____

_____

_____

_____

_____

_____

_____

_____

★

Day: _____ Date: ____ / ____ / ____

What is your least favorite part of your daily routine,
and why? How could you make it more enjoyable?

_____

_____

_____

_____

_____

_____

_____

_____

_____

_____

What was a notable or "aha" moment from today,
and why?

_____

_____

_____

_____

_____

_____

_____

_____

_____

★

Day: _____ Date: ____ / ____ / ____

If you were to meet yourself, what things would
you like about you?

_____

_____

_____

_____

_____

_____

_____

_____

_____

_____

What was a notable or "aha" moment from today,
and why?

_____

_____

_____

_____

_____

_____

_____

_____

_____

★

Day: _____ Date: ____ / ____ / ____

What are a few of the more notable moments from the past week, and in what ways (if any) will this change how you approach things moving forward?

_____

_____

_____

_____

_____

_____

_____

_____

_____

_____

_____

_____

_____

_____

_____

_____

_____

_____

★

Day: _____ Date: ____ / ____ / ____

What made you smile today,
and why?

_____

_____

_____

_____

_____

_____

_____

_____

_____

_____

What was a notable or "aha" moment from today,
and why?

_____

_____

_____

_____

_____

_____

_____

_____

_____

_____

★

Day: _____ Date: ____ / ____ / ____

What is one simple thing you could do every day that would
make a positive impact on some part of your life, and why?

_____

_____

_____

_____

_____

_____

_____

_____

_____

_____

What was a notable or "aha" moment from today,
and why?

_____

_____

_____

_____

_____

_____

_____

_____

_____

_____

★

All positive change, no matter how small, leads to massive amounts of growth over time.

Day: _____ Date: ____ / ____ / ____

Who was the last person you tried to impress, and why?

_____

_____

_____

_____

_____

_____

_____

_____

_____

What was a notable or "aha" moment from today, and why?

_____

_____

_____

_____

_____

_____

_____

_____

_____

★

Day: _____ Date: ____ / ____ / ____

*What feature do you like best (or least) about your
body, and why?*

_____

_____

_____

_____

_____

_____

_____

_____

_____

*What was a notable or "aha" moment from today,
and why?*

_____

_____

_____

_____

_____

_____

_____

_____

_____

★

Day: _____ Date: ____ / ____ / ____

What is one habit that you seem to have the most
trouble breaking? Why do you think this is?

_____

_____

_____

_____

_____

_____

_____

_____

What was a notable or "aha" moment from today,
and why?

_____

_____

_____

_____

_____

_____

_____

_____

_____

★

Day: _____ Date: ___ / ___ / ___

What is the latest life lesson you learned, and how will you apply it?

_____

_____

_____

_____

_____

_____

_____

_____

_____

_____

What was a notable or "aha" moment from today, and why?

_____

_____

_____

_____

_____

_____

_____

_____

_____

★

Day: _____ Date: ____ / ____ / ____

What are a few of the more notable moments from the past week, and in what ways (if any) will this change how you approach things moving forward?

_____

_____

_____

_____

_____

_____

_____

_____

_____

_____

_____

_____

_____

_____

_____

_____

_____

_____

_____

_____

★

Day: _____ Date: ____ / ____ / ____

What is one loving thing you can commit to doing for yourself during the next 24 hours, and why did you choose this thing?

_____

_____

_____

_____

_____

_____

_____

_____

_____

_____

What was a notable or "aha" moment from today, and why?

_____

_____

_____

_____

_____

_____

_____

_____

_____

_____

★

Day: _____ Date: ____ / ____ / ____

*When was the last time you had a breakdown or a
breakthrough, and what was the result?*

_____

_____

_____

_____

_____

_____

_____

_____

_____

_____

*What was a notable or "aha" moment from today,
and why?*

_____

_____

_____

_____

_____

_____

_____

_____

_____

★

Day: _____ Date: ____ / ____ / ____

What might someone envy about you or your life,
and why?

_____

_____

_____

_____

_____

_____

_____

_____

_____

_____

What was a notable or "aha" moment from today,
and why?

_____

_____

_____

_____

_____

_____

_____

_____

_____

★

Day: _____ Date: ____ / ____ / ____

What is one thing you feel the most content about
with yourself or your life, and why?

_____

_____

_____

_____

_____

_____

_____

_____

_____

What was a notable or "aha" moment from today,
and why?

_____

_____

_____

_____

_____

_____

_____

_____

_____

★

Day: _____ Date: ____ / ____ / ____

What has been a good decision you've made
lately, and why?

_____

_____

_____

_____

_____

_____

_____

_____

_____

_____

What was a notable or "aha" moment from today,
and why?

_____

_____

_____

_____

_____

_____

_____

_____

_____

★

Make decisions based
on what your future self
would thank you for.

Day: _____ Date: ___ / ___ / ___

What was your last small victory?

_____

_____

_____

_____

_____

_____

_____

_____

_____

What was a notable or "aha" moment from today,
and why?

_____

_____

_____

_____

_____

_____

_____

_____

_____

_____

★

Day: _____ Date: ____ / ____ / ____

What are a few of the more notable moments from the
past week, and in what ways (if any) will this change
how you approach things moving forward?

_____

_____

_____

_____

_____

_____

_____

_____

_____

_____

_____

_____

_____

_____

_____

_____

_____

_____

_____

★

Day: _____ Date: ____ / ____ / ____

What is some of the best (or worst) advice you've
ever received, and did you take it?

_____

_____

_____

_____

_____

_____

_____

_____

_____

_____

What was a notable or "aha" moment from today,
and why?

_____

_____

_____

_____

_____

_____

_____

_____

_____

★

Day: _____ Date: ____ / ____ / ____

If you could choose one person to be your mentor for the next year, who would you choose, and why?

_____

_____

_____

_____

_____

_____

_____

_____

_____

What was a notable or "aha" moment from today, and why?

_____

_____

_____

_____

_____

_____

_____

_____

_____

★

Day: _____ Date: ____ / ____ / ____

How are you feeling right now,
and why?

_____

_____

_____

_____

_____

_____

_____

_____

_____

_____

What was a notable or "aha" moment from today,
and why?

_____

_____

_____

_____

_____

_____

_____

_____

_____

★

Day: _____ Date: ____ / ____ / ____

When was the last time you got out of your comfort
zone? What did you do, and how did you feel about it?

_____

_____

_____

_____

_____

_____

_____

_____

_____

_____

What was a notable or "aha" moment from today,
and why?

_____

_____

_____

_____

_____

_____

_____

_____

_____

_____

✯

Personal growth and
embracing the discomfort of
change go
hand-in-hand.

Day: _____ Date: ____ / ____ / ____

When was the last time something didn't go as planned?
What happened, and what did you learn from it?

_____

_____

_____

_____

_____

_____

_____

_____

_____

_____

What was a notable or "aha" moment from today,
and why?

_____

_____

_____

_____

_____

_____

_____

_____

_____

_____

★

Day: _____ Date: ____ / ____ / ____

What are you grateful for today, and why?

_____

_____

_____

_____

_____

_____

_____

_____

_____

_____

What was a notable or "aha" moment from today,
and why?

_____

_____

_____

_____

_____

_____

_____

_____

_____

★

If you can't find anything
to be grateful for, you
aren't looking hard enough.

Day: _____ Date: ____ / ____ / ____

*What are a few of the more notable moments from the
past week, and in what ways (if any) will this change
how you approach things moving forward?*

_____

_____

_____

_____

_____

_____

_____

_____

_____

_____

_____

_____

_____

_____

_____

_____

_____

_____

★

Day: _____ Date: ___ / ___ / ___

What was the last intention or goal you set, and
why did you set it?

_____

_____

_____

_____

_____

_____

_____

_____

_____

_____

What was a notable or "aha" moment from today,
and why?

_____

_____

_____

_____

_____

_____

_____

_____

_____

_____

⭐

Day: _____ Date: ____ / ____ / ____

What is the last thing you did that made you feel good?

_____

_____

_____

_____

_____

_____

_____

_____

_____

What was a notable or "aha" moment from today, and why?

_____

_____

_____

_____

_____

_____

_____

_____

_____

★

Day: _____ Date: ____ / ____ / ____

What was the last thing your intuition told you?
Did you listen? Why or why not?

_____

_____

_____

_____

_____

_____

_____

_____

_____

_____

What was a notable or "aha" moment from today,
and why?

_____

_____

_____

_____

_____

_____

_____

_____

_____

★

Day: _____ Date: ____ / ____ / ____

When was the last time you had your feelings
hurt? What happened?

_____

_____

_____

_____

_____

_____

_____

_____

_____

What was a notable or "aha" moment from today,
and why?

_____

_____

_____

_____

_____

_____

_____

_____

_____

★

Day: _____ Date: ____ / ____ / ____

*What is the last new thing you tried, and how did
you feel about it?*

_____

_____

_____

_____

_____

_____

_____

_____

_____

_____

*What was a notable or "aha" moment from today,
and why?*

_____

_____

_____

_____

_____

_____

_____

_____

_____

★

Day: _____ Date: ____ / ____ / ____

*What are two things you hope to achieve during
the coming month, and why?*

_____

_____

_____

_____

_____

_____

_____

_____

_____

_____

*What was a notable or "aha" moment from today,
and why?*

_____

_____

_____

_____

_____

_____

_____

_____

_____

★

Day: _____ Date: ____ / ____ / ____

What are a few of the more notable moments from the past week, and in what ways (if any) will this change how you approach things moving forward?

_____

_____

_____

_____

_____

_____

_____

_____

_____

_____

_____

_____

_____

_____

_____

_____

_____

_____

★

Day: _____ Date: ____ / ____ / ____

What gives you a sense of peace,
and why?

_____

_____

_____

_____

_____

_____

_____

_____

_____

_____

What was a notable or "aha" moment from today,
and why?

_____

_____

_____

_____

_____

_____

_____

_____

_____

_____

★

Day: _____ Date: ____ / ____ / ____

What is one of the best decisions you've made
lately, and why?

_____

_____

_____

_____

_____

_____

_____

_____

_____

What was a notable or "aha" moment from today,
and why?

_____

_____

_____

_____

_____

_____

_____

_____

★

Day: _____ Date: ____ / ____ / ____

What main message do you think the last dream (or nightmare)
you had was trying to tell you, and why?

_____

_____

_____

_____

_____

_____

_____

_____

_____

_____

What was a notable or "aha" moment from today,
and why?

_____

_____

_____

_____

_____

_____

_____

_____

_____

✯

Day: _____ Date: ____ / ____ / ____

When was the last time you had fun? What did you do?

_____

_____

_____

_____

_____

_____

_____

_____

_____

What was a notable or "aha" moment from today, and why?

_____

_____

_____

_____

_____

_____

_____

_____

_____

★

Day: _____ Date: ____ / ____ / ____

*What is one thing you have been fearful of lately,
and why?*

_____

_____

_____

_____

_____

_____

_____

_____

_____

_____

*What was a notable or "aha" moment from today,
and why?*

_____

_____

_____

_____

_____

_____

_____

_____

_____

★

Day: _____ Date: ____ / ____ / ____

What is the healthiest or unhealthiest habit you
currently have, and what need is this habit serving?

_____

_____

_____

_____

_____

_____

_____

_____

_____

What was a notable or "aha" moment from today,
and why?

_____

_____

_____

_____

_____

_____

_____

_____

_____

★

We are only as
healthy as our coping
methods.

Day: _____ Date: ____ / ____ / ____

What are a few of the more notable moments from the past week, and in what ways (if any) will this change how you approach things moving forward?

_____

_____

_____

_____

_____

_____

_____

_____

_____

_____

_____

_____

_____

_____

_____

_____

_____

_____

_____

★

Day: _____ Date: ___ / ___ / ___

When was the last time you got really excited about
something? What was it, and why did it excite you?

_____

_____

_____

_____

_____

_____

_____

_____

_____

_____

What was a notable or "aha" moment from today,
and why?

_____

_____

_____

_____

_____

_____

_____

_____

_____

_____

★

Day: _____ Date: ____ / ____ / ____

When was the last time you got angry? What happened?

_____

_____

_____

_____

_____

_____

_____

_____

_____

_____

What was a notable or "aha" moment from today, and why?

_____

_____

_____

_____

_____

_____

_____

_____

_____

★

Day: _____ Date: ____ / ____ / ____

What books or websites have influenced you so far
this year, and why?

_____

_____

_____

_____

_____

_____

_____

_____

_____

_____

What was a notable or "aha" moment from today,
and why?

_____

_____

_____

_____

_____

_____

_____

_____

_____

_____

★

Day: _____ Date: ____ / ____ / ____

*What is the hardest change you've made so far
this year, and why?*

_____

_____

_____

_____

_____

_____

_____

_____

_____

_____

*What was a notable or "aha" moment from today,
and why?*

_____

_____

_____

_____

_____

_____

_____

_____

_____

★

Change is always
difficult, but it's necessary
for growth.

Day: _____ Date: ____ / ____ / ____

*What is one limiting belief you have that holds you back, and
what empowering belief could you replace it with?*

_____

_____

_____

_____

_____

_____

_____

_____

_____

_____

*What was a notable or "aha" moment from today,
and why?*

_____

_____

_____

_____

_____

_____

_____

_____

_____

★

Day: _____ Date: ____ / ____ / ____

If you continue to repeat what you are currently doing, where will you be in three years, and why?

_____

_____

_____

_____

_____

_____

_____

_____

_____

_____

What was a notable or "aha" moment from today, and why?

_____

_____

_____

_____

_____

_____

_____

_____

_____

_____

★

Day: _____ Date: ____ / ____ / ____

What are a few of the more notable moments from the past week, and in what ways (if any) will this change how you approach things moving forward?

_____

_____

_____

_____

_____

_____

_____

_____

_____

_____

_____

_____

_____

_____

_____

_____

_____

_____

_____

★

Day: _____ Date: ____ / ____ / ____

What is the last thing that little voice inside of you said
you could (or couldn't) do? How did you respond?

_____

_____

_____

_____

_____

_____

_____

_____

_____

_____

What was a notable or "aha" moment from today,
and why?

_____

_____

_____

_____

_____

_____

_____

_____

_____

★

Day: _____ Date: ____ / ____ / ____

What is the last "impossible" thing (as viewed by you or others) you accomplished, and why did you do it?

_____

_____

_____

_____

_____

_____

_____

_____

_____

_____

What was a notable or "aha" moment from today, and why?

_____

_____

_____

_____

_____

_____

_____

_____

_____

_____

⭐

Day: _____ Date: ____ / ____ / ____

What is the best advice you've been given so far
in life or so far this year, and why?

_____

_____

_____

_____

_____

_____

_____

_____

_____

_____

What was a notable or "aha" moment from today,
and why?

_____

_____

_____

_____

_____

_____

_____

_____

_____

_____

★

Day: _____ Date: ____ / ____ / ____

When was the last time you cried (or smiled) multiple
times for the same reason, and what was the reason?

_____

_____

_____

_____

_____

_____

_____

_____

_____

What was a notable or "aha" moment from today,
and why?

_____

_____

_____

_____

_____

_____

_____

_____

_____

★

Day: _____ Date: ____ / ____ / ____

What is one big lesson you learned over the past year?

_____

_____

_____

_____

_____

_____

_____

_____

_____

_____

What was a notable or "aha" moment from today, and why?

_____

_____

_____

_____

_____

_____

_____

_____

_____

★

Problems are just
challenges you haven't
overcome yet.

Day: _____ Date: ____ / ____ / ____

When did you last make time for self-care? What did you do, and why?

_____

_____

_____

_____

_____

_____

_____

_____

_____

_____

What was a notable or "aha" moment from today, and why?

_____

_____

_____

_____

_____

_____

_____

_____

_____

_____

★

Day: _____ Date: ____ / ____ / ____

What are a few of the more notable moments from the past week, and in what ways (if any) will this change how you approach things moving forward?

_____

_____

_____

_____

_____

_____

_____

_____

_____

_____

_____

_____

_____

_____

_____

_____

_____

_____

_____

★

Day: _____ Date: ____ / ____ / ____

What was the last lesson you learned from a
difficult person (or situation) in your life?

_____

_____

_____

_____

_____

_____

_____

_____

_____

What was a notable or "aha" moment from today,
and why?

_____

_____

_____

_____

_____

_____

_____

_____

_____

_____

★

Day: _____ Date: ___ / ___ / ___

What would your ideal Friday night be like, and why?

_____

_____

_____

_____

_____

_____

_____

_____

_____

What was a notable or "aha" moment from today, and why?

_____

_____

_____

_____

_____

_____

_____

_____

_____

★

Day: _____ Date: ____ / ____ / ____

What is the biggest problem you are facing right now, and why?

_____

_____

_____

_____

_____

_____

_____

_____

_____

_____

What was a notable or "aha" moment from today, and why?

_____

_____

_____

_____

_____

_____

_____

_____

_____

★

Day: _____ Date: ____ / ____ / ____

*How do you feel about the last person you spent
time with, and why?*

_____

_____

_____

_____

_____

_____

_____

_____

_____

*What was a notable or "aha" moment from today,
and why?*

_____

_____

_____

_____

_____

_____

_____

_____

_____

★

Day: _____ Date: ____ / ____ / ____

*In what ways have you been
creative lately?*

_____

_____

_____

_____

_____

_____

_____

_____

_____

_____

*What was a notable or "aha" moment from today,
and why?*

_____

_____

_____

_____

_____

_____

_____

_____

_____

_____

✭

Day: _____ Date: ____ / ____ / ____

When was the last time someone crossed one of your
boundaries? How did you handle it, and why?

_____

_____

_____

_____

_____

_____

_____

_____

_____

_____

What was a notable or "aha" moment from today,
and why?

_____

_____

_____

_____

_____

_____

_____

_____

_____

_____

★

Day: _____ Date: ____ / ____ / ____

*What are a few of the more notable moments from the
past week, and in what ways (if any) will this change
how you approach things moving forward?*

_____

_____

_____

_____

_____

_____

_____

_____

_____

_____

_____

_____

_____

_____

_____

_____

_____

_____

_____

★

Day: _____ Date: ____ / ____ / ____

What was the last healthy boundary you set, and
how did you feel about setting it?

_____

_____

_____

_____

_____

_____

_____

_____

_____

What was a notable or "aha" moment from today,
and why?

_____

_____

_____

_____

_____

_____

_____

_____

★

Day: _____ Date: ____ / ____ / ____

*What are two things you hope to achieve during
the coming month, and why?*

_____

_____

_____

_____

_____

_____

_____

_____

_____

*What was a notable or "aha" moment from today,
and why?*

_____

_____

_____

_____

_____

_____

_____

_____

★

Day: _____ Date: ____ / ____ / ____

If you could get one message out to the world this year,
what would it be, and why?

_____

_____

_____

_____

_____

_____

_____

_____

_____

_____

What was a notable or "aha" moment from today,
and why?

_____

_____

_____

_____

_____

_____

_____

_____

_____

★

Day: _____ Date: ____ / ____ / ____

What decision have you been hesitant to make,
and why?

_____

_____

_____

_____

_____

_____

_____

_____

_____

_____

What was a notable or "aha" moment from today,
and why?

_____

_____

_____

_____

_____

_____

_____

_____

_____

_____

★

Day: _____ Date: ____ / ____ / ____

What is one decision (no matter how big or small) you made so far this year that you really love, and why?

_____

_____

_____

_____

_____

_____

_____

_____

_____

_____

What was a notable or "aha" moment from today, and why?

_____

_____

_____

_____

_____

_____

_____

_____

_____

_____

★

Day: _____ Date: ____ / ____ / ____

Are you holding onto any anger or resentment? If so, what are you feeling angry or resentful about?

_____

_____

_____

_____

_____

_____

_____

_____

_____

_____

What was a notable or "aha" moment from today, and why?

_____

_____

_____

_____

_____

_____

_____

_____

_____

_____

★

Day: _____ Date: ____ / ____ / ____

*What are a few of the more notable moments from the
past week, and in what ways (if any) will this change
how you approach things moving forward?*

_____

_____

_____

_____

_____

_____

_____

_____

_____

_____

_____

_____

_____

_____

_____

_____

_____

_____

_____

_____

★

Day: _____ Date: ____ / ____ / ____

What do you like about your life right now, and why?

_____

_____

_____

_____

_____

_____

_____

_____

_____

_____

What was a notable or "aha" moment from today, and why?

_____

_____

_____

_____

_____

_____

_____

_____

_____

★

Day: _____ Date: ____ / ____ / ____

When was the last painful ending you experienced? In what
ways (if any) did it allow for a positive, new beginning?

_____

_____

_____

_____

_____

_____

_____

_____

_____

_____

What was a notable or "aha" moment from today,
and why?

_____

_____

_____

_____

_____

_____

_____

_____

_____

★

Day: _____ Date: ____ / ____ / ____

*When was the last time you had fun? What about
it was fun?*

_____

_____

_____

_____

_____

_____

_____

_____

_____

*What was a notable or "aha" moment from today,
and why?*

_____

_____

_____

_____

_____

_____

_____

_____

_____

★

Day: _____ Date: ____ / ____ / ____

*What is one thing you could do during the next 24 hours
that would positively impact your life, and why?*

_____

_____

_____

_____

_____

_____

_____

_____

_____

_____

*What was a notable or "aha" moment from today,
and why?*

_____

_____

_____

_____

_____

_____

_____

_____

_____

★

The fastest way to change your life is to start making a series of small, positive changes on a regular basis.

Day: _____ Date: ____ / ____ / ____

In what ways have you been creative or expressed
your individuality lately?

_____

_____

_____

_____

_____

_____

_____

_____

_____

What was a notable or "aha" moment from today,
and why?

_____

_____

_____

_____

_____

_____

_____

_____

_____

★

Day: _____ Date: ____ / ____ / ____

What fears have kept you stuck lately? What
would help you move past them?

_____

_____

_____

_____

_____

_____

_____

_____

_____

_____

What was a notable or "aha" moment from today,
and why?

_____

_____

_____

_____

_____

_____

_____

_____

_____

_____

★

Day: _____ Date: ____ / ____ / ____

What are a few of the more notable moments from the past week, and in what ways (if any) will this change how you approach things moving forward?

_____

_____

_____

_____

_____

_____

_____

_____

_____

_____

_____

_____

_____

_____

_____

_____

_____

_____

_____

★

Day: _____ Date: ____ / ____ / ____

*In what ways are you a friend (or an enemy) to
yourself?*

_____

_____

_____

_____

_____

_____

_____

_____

_____

_____

*What was a notable or "aha" moment from today,
and why?*

_____

_____

_____

_____

_____

_____

_____

_____

_____

★

Day: _____ Date: ____ / ____ / ____

What are two lessons you learned from your last
painful experience?

_____

_____

_____

_____

_____

_____

_____

_____

_____

_____

What was a notable or "aha" moment from today,
and why?

_____

_____

_____

_____

_____

_____

_____

_____

_____

_____

★

Day: _____ Date: ____ / ____ / ____

What was the last thing that made you smile, and why?

_____

_____

_____

_____

_____

_____

_____

_____

_____

_____

What was a notable or "aha" moment from today, and why?

_____

_____

_____

_____

_____

_____

_____

_____

_____

★

Day: _____ Date: ____ / ____ / ____

How has your mindset shifted lately,
and why?

_____

_____

_____

_____

_____

_____

_____

_____

_____

What was a notable or "aha" moment from today,
and why?

_____

_____

_____

_____

_____

_____

_____

_____

★

Day: _____ Date: ____ / ____ / ____

What is one thing you've learned (or accepted)
about yourself so far this year?

_____

_____

_____

_____

_____

_____

_____

_____

_____

What was a notable or "aha" moment from today,
and why?

_____

_____

_____

_____

_____

_____

_____

_____

_____

★

Day: _____ Date: ____ / ____ / ____

In what ways did you live an authentic
life today?

_____

_____

_____

_____

_____

_____

_____

_____

_____

_____

What was a notable or "aha" moment from today,
and why?

_____

_____

_____

_____

_____

_____

_____

_____

_____

_____

★

One of the hardest
things in life is being
ourselves.

Day: _____ Date: ____ / ____ / ____

What are a few of the more notable moments from the past week, and in what ways (if any) will this change how you approach things moving forward?

_____

_____

_____

_____

_____

_____

_____

_____

_____

_____

_____

_____

_____

_____

_____

_____

_____

_____

_____

★

Day: _____ Date: ___ / ___ / ___

*What is something you wish you had been taught
in school (or much sooner), and why?*

_____

_____

_____

_____

_____

_____

_____

_____

_____

_____

*What was a notable or "aha" moment from today,
and why?*

_____

_____

_____

_____

_____

_____

_____

_____

_____

★

Day: _____ Date: ___ / ___ / ___

How are you feeling right now,
and why?

_____

_____

_____

_____

_____

_____

_____

_____

_____

_____

What was a notable or "aha" moment from today,
and why?

_____

_____

_____

_____

_____

_____

_____

_____

_____

_____

★

Day: _____ Date: ____ / ____ / ____

*What is one thing you haven't done so far that
you'd really like to, and why?*

_____

_____

_____

_____

_____

_____

_____

_____

_____

_____

*What was a notable or "aha" moment from today,
and why?*

_____

_____

_____

_____

_____

_____

_____

_____

_____

★

Day: _____ Date: ____ / ____ / ____

*If your life was a book, who would be the main
characters in this chapter, and why?*

_____

_____

_____

_____

_____

_____

_____

_____

_____

*What was a notable or "aha" moment from today,
and why?*

_____

_____

_____

_____

_____

_____

_____

_____

_____

_____

★

Day: _____ Date: ___ / ___ / ___

How have you been spending the majority of your free time lately, and why?

_____

_____

_____

_____

_____

_____

_____

_____

_____

_____

What was a notable or "aha" moment from today, and why?

_____

_____

_____

_____

_____

_____

_____

_____

_____

★

Day: _____ Date: ___ / ___ / ___

What is your biggest weakness,
and why?

_____

_____

_____

_____

_____

_____

_____

_____

_____

_____

What was a notable or "aha" moment from today,
and why?

_____

_____

_____

_____

_____

_____

_____

_____

_____

_____

★

Day: _____ Date: ____ / ____ / ____

What are a few of the more notable moments from the past week, and in what ways (if any) will this change how you approach things moving forward?

_____

_____

_____

_____

_____

_____

_____

_____

_____

_____

_____

_____

_____

_____

_____

_____

_____

_____

_____

★

Day: _____ Date: ____ / ____ / ____

*What are some of your talents, and how have you
expressed them so far this year?*

_____

_____

_____

_____

_____

_____

_____

_____

_____

*What was a notable or "aha" moment from today,
and why?*

_____

_____

_____

_____

_____

_____

_____

_____

_____

★

Day: _____ Date: ____ / ____ / ____

If you had a magic wand, what two things in your
life would you change, and why?

_____

_____

_____

_____

_____

_____

_____

_____

_____

_____

What was a notable or "aha" moment from today,
and why?

_____

_____

_____

_____

_____

_____

_____

_____

_____

★

Day: _____ Date: ____ / ____ / ____

When was the last time you lied to yourself (or someone else)? Why did you lie, and what did you lie about?

_____

_____

_____

_____

_____

_____

_____

_____

_____

What was a notable or "aha" moment from today, and why?

_____

_____

_____

_____

_____

_____

_____

_____

_____

⭐

Day: _____ Date: ___ / ___ / ___

What are two things you hope to achieve during
the coming month, and why?

_____

_____

_____

_____

_____

_____

_____

_____

_____

_____

What was a notable or "aha" moment from today,
and why?

_____

_____

_____

_____

_____

_____

_____

_____

_____

★

Day: _____ Date: ____ / ____ / ____

Do you like where you live?
Why or why not?

_____

_____

_____

_____

_____

_____

_____

_____

_____

What was a notable or "aha" moment from today,
and why?

_____

_____

_____

_____

_____

_____

_____

_____

_____

★

Day: _____ Date: ____ / ____ / ____

What kind of environment (home, work, etc.) do
you thrive in, and why?

_____

_____

_____

_____

_____

_____

_____

_____

_____

What was a notable or "aha" moment from today,
and why?

_____

_____

_____

_____

_____

_____

_____

_____

_____

★

Day: _____ Date: ____ / ____ / ____

*What are a few of the more notable moments from the
past week, and in what ways (if any) will this change
how you approach things moving forward?*

_____

_____

_____

_____

_____

_____

_____

_____

_____

_____

_____

_____

_____

_____

_____

_____

_____

_____

⭐

Day: _____ Date: ____ / ____ / ____

*What is the last thing you learned, and how will
you apply it?*

_____

_____

_____

_____

_____

_____

_____

_____

_____

*What was a notable or "aha" moment from today,
and why?*

_____

_____

_____

_____

_____

_____

_____

_____

_____

★

Life is full of lessons. Some are painful and some are beautiful. We step into our power when we can squeeze as many lessons as we can out of both types of experiences.

Day: _____ Date: ____ / ____ / ____

*If you could live anywhere in the world, where
would you want to live, and why?*

_____

_____

_____

_____

_____

_____

_____

_____

_____

*What was a notable or "aha" moment from today,
and why?*

_____

_____

_____

_____

_____

_____

_____

_____

★

Day: _____ Date: ____ / ____ / ____

What part of your daily routine would you like to change or get rid of, and why?

_____

_____

_____

_____

_____

_____

_____

_____

_____

What was a notable or "aha" moment from today, and why?

_____

_____

_____

_____

_____

_____

_____

_____

_____

★

Day: _____ Date: ____ / ____ / ____

*How did you treat the last person you interacted
with, and why?*

_____

_____

_____

_____

_____

_____

_____

_____

_____

*What was a notable or "aha" moment from today,
and why?*

_____

_____

_____

_____

_____

_____

_____

_____

_____

Day: _____ Date: ____ / ____ / ____

Out of all the people you've spent time with this year, who has the most solid character and what makes it so solid?

_____

_____

_____

_____

_____

_____

_____

_____

_____

_____

What was a notable or "aha" moment from today, and why?

_____

_____

_____

_____

_____

_____

_____

_____

_____

★

Day: _____ Date: ____ / ____ / ____

*What is the nicest thing you've done for someone
this week, and why?*

_____

_____

_____

_____

_____

_____

_____

_____

_____

*What was a notable or "aha" moment from today,
and why?*

_____

_____

_____

_____

_____

_____

_____

_____

_____

✮

Day: _____ Date: ____ / ____ / ____

What are a few of the more notable moments from the past week, and in what ways (if any) will this change how you approach things moving forward?

_____

_____

_____

_____

_____

_____

_____

_____

_____

_____

_____

_____

_____

_____

_____

_____

_____

_____

⭐

Day: _____ Date: ____ / ____ / ____

*What might the last people you spent time with
think is unique or "quirky" about you, and why?*

_____

_____

_____

_____

_____

_____

_____

_____

_____

*What was a notable or "aha" moment from today,
and why?*

_____

_____

_____

_____

_____

_____

_____

_____

_____

✫

Day: _____ Date: ___ / ___ / ___

What distractions are you needing or wanting to
cut out of your life, and why?

_____

_____

_____

_____

_____

_____

_____

_____

_____

_____

What was a notable or "aha" moment from today,
and why?

_____

_____

_____

_____

_____

_____

_____

_____

_____

_____

★

Day: _____ Date: ____ / ____ / ____

*What has been the hardest truth you've tried to
face lately, and why?*

_____

_____

_____

_____

_____

_____

_____

_____

_____

_____

*What was a notable or "aha" moment from today,
and why?*

_____

_____

_____

_____

_____

_____

_____

_____

_____

_____

★

One of the hardest
things in life is being
honest with ourselves.

Day: _____ Date: ___ / ___ / ___

In what ways have you sabotaged yourself during the
past (or this year), and why do you think this is?

_____

_____

_____

_____

_____

_____

_____

_____

_____

_____

What was a notable or "aha" moment from today,
and why?

_____

_____

_____

_____

_____

_____

_____

_____

_____

_____

★

Day: _____ Date: ___ / ___ / ___

*One year from today, how do you think your life will
be different due to your current decisions, and why?*

_____

_____

_____

_____

_____

_____

_____

_____

_____

_____

*What was a notable or "aha" moment from today,
and why?*

_____

_____

_____

_____

_____

_____

_____

_____

_____

_____

⭐

Day: _____ Date: ____ / ____ / ____

*By the end of this three-year journal, how do you
think your life will be different, and why?*

_____

_____

_____

_____

_____

_____

_____

_____

_____

_____

*What was a notable or "aha" moment from today,
and why?*

_____

_____

_____

_____

_____

_____

_____

_____

_____

★

Day: _____ Date: ____ / ____ / ____

What are a few of the more notable moments from the past week, and in what ways (if any) will this change how you approach things moving forward?

_____

_____

_____

_____

_____

_____

_____

_____

_____

_____

_____

_____

_____

_____

_____

_____

_____

_____

_____

★

Day: _____ Date: ____ / ____ / ____

What have you lost interest in recently,
and why?

_____

_____

_____

_____

_____

_____

_____

_____

_____

What was a notable or "aha" moment from today,
and why?

_____

_____

_____

_____

_____

_____

_____

_____

_____

★

Day: _____ Date: ____ / ____ / ____

How are you feeling right now,
and why?

_____

_____

_____

_____

_____

_____

_____

_____

_____

_____

What was a notable or "aha" moment from today,
and why?

_____

_____

_____

_____

_____

_____

_____

_____

_____

_____

★

Day: _____ Date: ____ / ____ / ____

What was the last thing to stress you out, and why?

_____

_____

_____

_____

_____

_____

_____

_____

_____

What was a notable or "aha" moment from today, and why?

_____

_____

_____

_____

_____

_____

_____

_____

_____

★

Day: _____ Date: ___ / ___ / ___

How has your mindset shifted lately,
and why?

_____

_____

_____

_____

_____

_____

_____

_____

_____

_____

What was a notable or "aha" moment from today,
and why?

_____

_____

_____

_____

_____

_____

_____

_____

_____

★

Day: _____ Date: ____ / ____ / ____

*What action that you're currently taking benefits
your life the most, and why?*

_____

_____

_____

_____

_____

_____

_____

_____

_____

*What was a notable or "aha" moment from today,
and why?*

_____

_____

_____

_____

_____

_____

_____

_____

_____

★

Day: _____ Date: ___ / ___ / ___

What traits do you admire most about the last
person you spent time with, and why?

_____

_____

_____

_____

_____

_____

_____

_____

_____

What was a notable or "aha" moment from today,
and why?

_____

_____

_____

_____

_____

_____

_____

_____

_____

★

Day:_____ Date:____ / ____ / ____

What are a few of the more notable moments from the past week, and in what ways (if any) will this change how you approach things moving forward?

_____

_____

_____

_____

_____

_____

_____

_____

_____

_____

_____

_____

_____

_____

_____

_____

_____

★

Day: _____ Date: ____ / ____ / ____

What was the last thing you did out of fear, guilt,
or obligation, and why?

_____

_____

_____

_____

_____

_____

_____

_____

_____

_____

What was a notable or "aha" moment from today,
and why?

_____

_____

_____

_____

_____

_____

_____

_____

_____

★

Day: _____ Date: ____ / ____ / ____

When was the last time you had a boundary crossed?
Who crossed it, and what did you do about it?

_____

_____

_____

_____

_____

_____

_____

_____

_____

_____

What was a notable or "aha" moment from today,
and why?

_____

_____

_____

_____

_____

_____

_____

_____

_____

★

Day: _____ Date: ____ / ____ / ____

*What is one thing you would like to start doing
daily, and why?*

_____

_____

_____

_____

_____

_____

_____

_____

_____

_____

*What was a notable or "aha" moment from today,
and why?*

_____

_____

_____

_____

_____

_____

_____

_____

_____

★

Day: _____ Date: ____ / ____ / ____

*What is one thing that is different about who you
are today compared to last year, and why?*

_____

_____

_____

_____

_____

_____

_____

_____

_____

*What was a notable or "aha" moment from today,
and why?*

_____

_____

_____

_____

_____

_____

_____

_____

_____

Day: _____ Date: ____ / ____ / ____

When was the last time you got upset? How did you handle it, and would you handle it differently next time?

_____

_____

_____

_____

_____

_____

_____

_____

_____

_____

What was a notable or "aha" moment from today, and why?

_____

_____

_____

_____

_____

_____

_____

_____

_____

_____

✫

Day: _____ Date: ____ / ____ / ____

Have any of your beliefs changed lately? If so,
how and why?

_____

_____

_____

_____

_____

_____

_____

_____

_____

_____

What was a notable or "aha" moment from today,
and why?

_____

_____

_____

_____

_____

_____

_____

_____

_____

★

Day: _____ Date: ____ / ____ / ____

*What are two things you hope to achieve during
the coming month, and why?*

_____

_____

_____

_____

_____

_____

_____

_____

_____

*What was a notable or "aha" moment from today,
and why?*

_____

_____

_____

_____

_____

_____

_____

_____

_____

★

Day: _____ Date:____ /____ /____

What are a few of the more notable moments from the past week, and in what ways (if any) will this change how you approach things moving forward?

_____

_____

_____

_____

_____

_____

_____

_____

_____

_____

_____

_____

_____

_____

_____

_____

_____

_____

✫

Day: _____ Date: ____ / ____ / ____

*What are some ways you have lived life on your
own terms lately?*

_____

_____

_____

_____

_____

_____

_____

_____

_____

*What was a notable or "aha" moment from today,
and why?*

_____

_____

_____

_____

_____

_____

_____

_____

_____

_____

★

Day: _____ Date: ___ / ___ / ___

Where did you last travel, and in what ways did it change you?

_____

_____

_____

_____

_____

_____

_____

_____

_____

_____

What was a notable or "aha" moment from today, and why?

_____

_____

_____

_____

_____

_____

_____

_____

_____

✶

The best part about traveling isn't so much discovering new places, but discovering new things within ourselves.

Day: _____ Date: ____ / ____ / ____

What is one quality you don't like about yourself that
surfaced recently? What is it, and what happened?

_____

_____

_____

_____

_____

_____

_____

_____

_____

What was a notable or "aha" moment from today,
and why?

_____

_____

_____

_____

_____

_____

_____

_____

_____

_____

★

Day: _____ Date: ____ / ____ / ____

Who is the most empowering (or disempowering)
person in your life, and why do you spend time with them?

_____

_____

_____

_____

_____

_____

_____

_____

_____

_____

What was a notable or "aha" moment from today,
and why?

_____

_____

_____

_____

_____

_____

_____

_____

_____

★

Day: _____ Date: ____ / ____ / ____

What was the last unhealthy situation you walked
away from lately? What made it unhealthy?

_____

_____

_____

_____

_____

_____

_____

_____

_____

_____

What was a notable or "aha" moment from today,
and why?

_____

_____

_____

_____

_____

_____

_____

_____

_____

⭐

Day: _____ Date: ___ / ___ / ___

What are a few of the more notable moments from the past week, and in what ways (if any) will this change how you approach things moving forward?

_____

_____

_____

_____

_____

_____

_____

_____

_____

_____

_____

_____

_____

_____

_____

_____

_____

_____

_____

_____

★

Day: _____ Date: ____ / ____ / ____

What are some of your current goals,
and why?

_____

_____

_____

_____

_____

_____

_____

_____

_____

_____

What was a notable or "aha" moment from today,
and why?

_____

_____

_____

_____

_____

_____

_____

_____

_____

_____

★

Day: _____ Date: ___ / ___ / ___

What most excites you right now,
and why?

_____

_____

_____

_____

_____

_____

_____

_____

_____

What was a notable or "aha" moment from today,
and why?

_____

_____

_____

_____

_____

_____

_____

_____

_____

✯

Day: _____ Date: ____ / ____ / ____

*In what two ways could you take better care of
yourself?*

_____

_____

_____

_____

_____

_____

_____

_____

_____

*What was a notable or "aha" moment from today,
and why?*

_____

_____

_____

_____

_____

_____

_____

_____

_____

★

Day: _____ Date: ____ / ____ / ____

If you could have a conversation with your younger self, what are two things you would say, and why?

_____

_____

_____

_____

_____

_____

_____

_____

_____

What was a notable or "aha" moment from today, and why?

_____

_____

_____

_____

_____

_____

_____

_____

_____

★

Day: _____ Date: ____ / ____ / ____

What is one empowering value or belief you've
cultivated over the past year, and why?

_____

_____

_____

_____

_____

_____

_____

_____

_____

What was a notable or "aha" moment from today,
and why?

_____

_____

_____

_____

_____

_____

_____

_____

_____

★

Day: _____ Date: ____ / ____ / ____

*What is a disempowering belief you have? What is
an empowering belief you could replace it with?*

_____

_____

_____

_____

_____

_____

_____

_____

_____

*What was a notable or "aha" moment from today,
and why?*

_____

_____

_____

_____

_____

_____

_____

_____

_____

_____

★

Day: _____ Date: ____ / ____ / ____

What are a few of the more notable moments from the past week, and in what ways (if any) will this change how you approach things moving forward?

_____

_____

_____

_____

_____

_____

_____

_____

_____

_____

_____

_____

_____

_____

_____

_____

_____

_____

_____

_____

⭐

Day: _____ Date: ___ / ___ / ___

When was the last time you felt stressed, and how did you handle it?

_____

_____

_____

_____

_____

_____

_____

_____

_____

_____

What was a notable or "aha" moment from today, and why?

_____

_____

_____

_____

_____

_____

_____

_____

_____

_____

✮

Day: _____ Date: ____ / ____ / ____

How are you feeling right now,
and why?

_____

_____

_____

_____

_____

_____

_____

_____

_____

_____

What was a notable or "aha" moment from today,
and why?

_____

_____

_____

_____

_____

_____

_____

_____

_____

_____

★

Day: _____ Date: ____ / ____ / ____

When was the last time you felt depressed, and
how could you tell?

_____

_____

_____

_____

_____

_____

_____

_____

_____

What was a notable or "aha" moment from today,
and why?

_____

_____

_____

_____

_____

_____

_____

_____

_____

★

Day: _____ Date: ____ / ____ / ____

What is one major lesson learned or "aha" moment you've
had so far this year, and how did it change you?

_____

_____

_____

_____

_____

_____

_____

_____

_____

What was a notable or "aha" moment from today,
and why?

_____

_____

_____

_____

_____

_____

_____

_____

_____

★

Day: _____ Date: ____ / ____ / ____

*If you could have done one thing differently this
past month or year, what would it be, and why?*

_____

_____

_____

_____

_____

_____

_____

_____

_____

_____

*What was a notable or "aha" moment from today,
and why?*

_____

_____

_____

_____

_____

_____

_____

_____

_____

_____

★

Day: _____ Date: ___ / ___ / ___

What is one topic you think about often, and why
do you think that is?

_____

_____

_____

_____

_____

_____

_____

_____

_____

_____

What was a notable or "aha" moment from today,
and why?

_____

_____

_____

_____

_____

_____

_____

_____

_____

_____

★

Day: _____ Date: ____ / ____ / ____

What are a few of the more notable moments from the past week, and in what ways (if any) will this change how you approach things moving forward?

_____

_____

_____

_____

_____

_____

_____

_____

_____

_____

_____

_____

_____

_____

_____

_____

_____

_____

_____

_____

★

Day: _____ Date: ____ / ____ / ____

*What is the last thing you discovered about
yourself, and how do you feel about it?*

_____

_____

_____

_____

_____

_____

_____

_____

_____

*What was a notable or "aha" moment from today,
and why?*

_____

_____

_____

_____

_____

_____

_____

_____

_____

★

Self-discovery is often an intense, fascinating, and sometimes depressing journey, but it's necessary if we are going to live an authentic life.

Day: _____ Date: ____ / ____ / ____

*What was the last compliment you received? How
did you feel about it?*

_____

_____

_____

_____

_____

_____

_____

_____

_____

*What was a notable or "aha" moment from today,
and why?*

_____

_____

_____

_____

_____

_____

_____

_____

_____

★

Day: _____ Date: ____ / ____ / ____

*What was the last big idea you had? Will you be
acting on it? Why or why not?*

_____

_____

_____

_____

_____

_____

_____

_____

_____

_____

*What was a notable or "aha" moment from today,
and why?*

_____

_____

_____

_____

_____

_____

_____

_____

_____

_____

★

Day: _____ Date: ___ / ___ / ___

What is the biggest change you want to make in
your life right now, and why?

_____

_____

_____

_____

_____

_____

_____

_____

_____

_____

What was a notable or "aha" moment from today,
and why?

_____

_____

_____

_____

_____

_____

_____

_____

_____

★

Day: _____ Date: ___ / ___ / ___

When did you last make time for self-care? What did you do, and why?

_____

_____

_____

_____

_____

_____

_____

_____

_____

_____

What was a notable or "aha" moment from today, and why?

_____

_____

_____

_____

_____

_____

_____

_____

_____

_____

★

Day: _____ Date: ____ / ____ / ____

What do you hope isn't in your life a year from now, and why?

_____

_____

_____

_____

_____

_____

_____

_____

_____

_____

What was a notable or "aha" moment from today, and why?

_____

_____

_____

_____

_____

_____

_____

_____

_____

_____

★

Day: _____ Date: ____ / ____ / ____

What are a few of the more notable moments from the past week, and in what ways (if any) will this change how you approach things moving forward?

_____

_____

_____

_____

_____

_____

_____

_____

_____

_____

_____

_____

_____

_____

_____

_____

_____

_____

_____

_____

★

Day: _____ Date: ____ / ____ / ____

*Are you feeling frustrated about anything? If so,
what and why?*

_____

_____

_____

_____

_____

_____

_____

_____

_____

_____

*What was a notable or "aha" moment from today,
and why?*

_____

_____

_____

_____

_____

_____

_____

_____

_____

★

Day: _____ Date: ____ / ____ / ____

When was the last time you felt confident, and why?

_____

_____

_____

_____

_____

_____

_____

_____

_____

What was a notable or "aha" moment from today, and why?

_____

_____

_____

_____

_____

_____

_____

_____

_____

★

Day: _____ Date: ____ / ____ / ____

*What are two things you hope to achieve during
the coming month, and why?*

_____

_____

_____

_____

_____

_____

_____

_____

_____

_____

*What was a notable or "aha" moment from today,
and why?*

_____

_____

_____

_____

_____

_____

_____

_____

_____

★

Day: _____ Date: ____ / ____ / ____

When was the last time you felt anxious? What
physical or emotional signs did you have?

_____

_____

_____

_____

_____

_____

_____

_____

_____

What was a notable or "aha" moment from today,
and why?

_____

_____

_____

_____

_____

_____

_____

_____

_____

✯

Day: _____ Date: ____ / ____ / ____

*When was the last good decision you made, and
what made it good?*

_____

_____

_____

_____

_____

_____

_____

_____

_____

*What was a notable or "aha" moment from today,
and why?*

_____

_____

_____

_____

_____

_____

_____

_____

_____

★

Day: _____ Date: ____ / ____ / ____

What do you most often daydream about, and why
do you think this is?

_____

_____

_____

_____

_____

_____

_____

_____

_____

What was a notable or "aha" moment from today,
and why?

_____

_____

_____

_____

_____

_____

_____

_____

_____

★

Day: _____ Date:____ / ____ / ____

What are a few of the more notable moments from the past week, and in what ways (if any) will this change how you approach things moving forward?

_____

_____

_____

_____

_____

_____

_____

_____

_____

_____

_____

_____

_____

_____

_____

_____

_____

_____

_____

Day: _____ Date: ____ / ____ / ____

When was the last time you found yourself doing the same thing over and over, expecting a different result, and why?

_____

_____

_____

_____

_____

_____

_____

_____

_____

What was a notable or "aha" moment from today, and why?

_____

_____

_____

_____

_____

_____

_____

_____

_____

⭐

Day: _____ Date: ___ / ___ / ___

What have you been insecure about lately, and why?

_____

_____

_____

_____

_____

_____

_____

_____

_____

_____

What was a notable or "aha" moment from today, and why?

_____

_____

_____

_____

_____

_____

_____

_____

_____

★

Day: _____ Date: ___ / ___ / ___

When was the last time you felt your life was off-track in some way? How could you tell, and what did you do about it?

_____

_____

_____

_____

_____

_____

_____

_____

_____

What was a notable or "aha" moment from today, and why?

_____

_____

_____

_____

_____

_____

_____

_____

_____

★

Day: _____ Date: ____ / ____ / ____

*When was the last time you felt things in your life
were on the right track, and how did you feel?*

_____

_____

_____

_____

_____

_____

_____

_____

_____

*What was a notable or "aha" moment from today,
and why?*

_____

_____

_____

_____

_____

_____

_____

_____

_____

★

Day: _____ Date: ____ / ____ / ____

*When was the last time you had
a good laugh?*

_____

_____

_____

_____

_____

_____

_____

_____

_____

*What was a notable or "aha" moment from today,
and why?*

_____

_____

_____

_____

_____

_____

_____

_____

_____

★

Day: _____ Date: ____ / ____ / ____

*What has been the biggest life-changing event so
far this year, and why?*

_____

_____

_____

_____

_____

_____

_____

_____

_____

_____

*What was a notable or "aha" moment from today,
and why?*

_____

_____

_____

_____

_____

_____

_____

_____

_____

_____

★

Day: _____ Date: ____ / ____ / ____

What are a few of the more notable moments from the past week, and in what ways (if any) will this change how you approach things moving forward?

_____

_____

_____

_____

_____

_____

_____

_____

_____

_____

_____

_____

_____

_____

_____

_____

_____

_____

_____

★

Day: _____ Date: ____ / ____ / ____

What has been a limiting belief that has held you back lately,
and why?

_____

_____

_____

_____

_____

_____

_____

_____

_____

_____

What was a notable or "aha" moment from today,
and why?

_____

_____

_____

_____

_____

_____

_____

_____

_____

★

Day: _____ Date: ____ / ____ / ____

Outside of food, clothing, and shelter, what are some of the necessary things in your life, and why?

_____

_____

_____

_____

_____

_____

_____

_____

_____

_____

What was a notable or "aha" moment from today, and why?

_____

_____

_____

_____

_____

_____

_____

_____

_____

_____

✫

Avoidance is often
fear dressed up like
procrastination.

Day: _____ Date: ____ / ____ / ____

What have you been putting off,
and why?

_____

_____

_____

_____

_____

_____

_____

_____

_____

_____

What was a notable or "aha" moment from today,
and why?

_____

_____

_____

_____

_____

_____

_____

_____

_____

_____

★

Day: _____ Date: ____ / ____ / ____

When was the last time you felt really determined
about something, and why?

_____

_____

_____

_____

_____

_____

_____

_____

_____

What was a notable or "aha" moment from today,
and why?

_____

_____

_____

_____

_____

_____

_____

_____

_____

★

Day: _____ Date: ____ / ____ / ____

How did you handle your feelings the last time you got angry?
And what might you do differently (if anything) in the future?

_____

_____

_____

_____

_____

_____

_____

_____

_____

_____

What was a notable or "aha" moment from today,
and why?

_____

_____

_____

_____

_____

_____

_____

_____

_____

★

Day: _____ Date: ___ / ___ / ___

When was the last time you compared yourself to
someone else, and what was the comparison you made?

_____

_____

_____

_____

_____

_____

_____

_____

_____

_____

What was a notable or "aha" moment from today,
and why?

_____

_____

_____

_____

_____

_____

_____

_____

_____

_____

★

Day: _____ Date: ____ / ____ / ____

*What are a few of the more notable moments from the
past week, and in what ways (if any) will this change
how you approach things moving forward?*

_____

_____

_____

_____

_____

_____

_____

_____

_____

_____

_____

_____

_____

_____

_____

_____

_____

_____

_____

★

Day: _____ Date: ____ / ____ / ____

*When was the last time you were really upset by
something, and why?*

_____

_____

_____

_____

_____

_____

_____

_____

_____

*What was a notable or "aha" moment from today,
and why?*

_____

_____

_____

_____

_____

_____

_____

_____

_____

★

Day: _____ Date: ___ / ___ / ___

What kind of music, talk radio, or podcasts have
you been listening to lately, and why?

_____

_____

_____

_____

_____

_____

_____

_____

_____

What was a notable or "aha" moment from today,
and why?

_____

_____

_____

_____

_____

_____

_____

_____

_____

★

Day: _____ Date: ____ / ____ / ____

What was the last good thing to happen to you,
and why was it good?

_____

_____

_____

_____

_____

_____

_____

_____

_____

_____

What was a notable or "aha" moment from today,
and why?

_____

_____

_____

_____

_____

_____

_____

_____

_____

_____

★

Day: _____ Date: ____ / ____ / ____

What are the two most recent ways you have
treated yourself with value?

_____

_____

_____

_____

_____

_____

_____

_____

_____

What was a notable or "aha" moment from today,
and why?

_____

_____

_____

_____

_____

_____

_____

_____

_____

★

Day: _____ Date: ___ / ___ / ___

*When was the last time you got upset with a
friend, and what happened?*

_____

_____

_____

_____

_____

_____

_____

_____

_____

_____

*What was a notable or "aha" moment from today,
and why?*

_____

_____

_____

_____

_____

_____

_____

_____

_____

★

Day: _____ Date: ___ / ___ / ___

If time and money weren't an issue, what would you do, and why?

_____

_____

_____

_____

_____

_____

_____

_____

_____

_____

What was a notable or "aha" moment from today, and why?

_____

_____

_____

_____

_____

_____

_____

_____

_____

_____

✪

Day: _____ Date: ___ / ___ / ___

What are a few of the more notable moments from the past week, and in what ways (if any) will this change how you approach things moving forward?

_____

_____

_____

_____

_____

_____

_____

_____

_____

_____

_____

_____

_____

_____

_____

_____

_____

_____

_____

_____

✭

Day: _____ Date: ____ / ____ / ____

What is the last empowering thing you told your-
self (or someone else), and what was the result?

_____

_____

_____

_____

_____

_____

_____

_____

_____

What was a notable or "aha" moment from today,
and why?

_____

_____

_____

_____

_____

_____

_____

_____

_____

★

Day: _____ Date: ___ / ___ / ___

What is the last disempowering thing you told yourself
(or someone else), and what was the result?

_____

_____

_____

_____

_____

_____

_____

_____

_____

_____

What was a notable or "aha" moment from today,
and why?

_____

_____

_____

_____

_____

_____

_____

_____

_____

★

Day: _____ Date: ____ / ____ / ____

If someone gave you $10,000 today, how would
you spend it, and why?

_____

_____

_____

_____

_____

_____

_____

_____

_____

_____

What was a notable or "aha" moment from today,
and why?

_____

_____

_____

_____

_____

_____

_____

_____

_____

★

Day: _____ Date: ____ / ____ / ____

When was the last time you felt relieved,
and why?

_____

_____

_____

_____

_____

_____

_____

_____

_____

_____

What was a notable or "aha" moment from today,
and why?

_____

_____

_____

_____

_____

_____

_____

_____

_____

_____

✫

Day: _____ Date: ____ / ____ / ____

*What are two things you hope to achieve during
the coming month, and why?*

_____

_____

_____

_____

_____

_____

_____

_____

_____

_____

*What was a notable or "aha" moment from today,
and why?*

_____

_____

_____

_____

_____

_____

_____

_____

_____

_____

★

Day: _____ Date: ____ / ____ / ____

What is one change you could make to get rid of
some of the stress in your life?

_____

_____

_____

_____

_____

_____

_____

_____

_____

_____

What was a notable or "aha" moment from today,
and why?

_____

_____

_____

_____

_____

_____

_____

_____

_____

_____

✯

There are a few things that I know for certain in this life, and one of them is that you will never look back on any stressful events in your life and think to yourself, "Boy, I really wish I would have worried about that more."

Day: _____ Date: ___ / ___ / ___

What are a few of the more notable moments from the past week, and in what ways (if any) will this change how you approach things moving forward?

_____

_____

_____

_____

_____

_____

_____

_____

_____

_____

_____

_____

_____

_____

_____

_____

_____

Day: _____ Date: ____ / ____ / ____

What is the most embarrassing thing to happen to you so far this year, and why?

_____

_____

_____

_____

_____

_____

_____

_____

_____

What was a notable or "aha" moment from today, and why?

_____

_____

_____

_____

_____

_____

_____

_____

_____

★

Day: _____ Date: ___ / ___ / ___

If you had an extra three hours every day, how
would you spend them, and why?

_____

_____

_____

_____

_____

_____

_____

_____

_____

_____

What was a notable or "aha" moment from today,
and why?

_____

_____

_____

_____

_____

_____

_____

_____

_____

✫

Day: _____ Date: ____ / ____ / ____

*What is the most empowering thing you've done
for yourself lately, and why?*

_____

_____

_____

_____

_____

_____

_____

_____

_____

*What was a notable or "aha" moment from today,
and why?*

_____

_____

_____

_____

_____

_____

_____

_____

_____

★

Day: _____ Date: ____ / ____ / ____

What book have you read (this year or in general)
that changed your life, and why?

_____

_____

_____

_____

_____

_____

_____

_____

_____

_____

What was a notable or "aha" moment from today,
and why?

_____

_____

_____

_____

_____

_____

_____

_____

_____

★

Day: _____ Date: ____ / ____ / ____

*When was the last time you stepped outside of your
comfort zone? What did you do, and how did it change you?*

_____

_____

_____

_____

_____

_____

_____

_____

_____

*What was a notable or "aha" moment from today,
and why?*

_____

_____

_____

_____

_____

_____

_____

_____

_____

⭐

Day: _____ Date: ____ / ____ / ____

If you didn't know your age, how old would you
think you are, and why?

_____

_____

_____

_____

_____

_____

_____

_____

_____

What was a notable or "aha" moment from today,
and why?

_____

_____

_____

_____

_____

_____

_____

_____

★

Day: _____ Date: ____ / ____ / ____

What are a few of the more notable moments from the past week, and in what ways (if any) will this change how you approach things moving forward?

_____

_____

_____

_____

_____

_____

_____

_____

_____

_____

_____

_____

_____

_____

_____

_____

_____

_____

_____

★

Day: _____ Date: ____ / ____ / ____

What are two things you've learned about
yourself lately?

_____

_____

_____

_____

_____

_____

_____

_____

_____

_____

What was a notable or "aha" moment from today,
and why?

_____

_____

_____

_____

_____

_____

_____

_____

_____

★

Day: _____ Date: ___ / ___ / ___

*What are one or two things you do differently from
the last person you spent time with, and why?*

_____

_____

_____

_____

_____

_____

_____

_____

_____

*What was a notable or "aha" moment from today,
and why?*

_____

_____

_____

_____

_____

_____

_____

_____

_____

★

Day: _____ Date: ____ / ____ / ____

What was the last thing you were deeply
passionate about, and why?

_____

_____

_____

_____

_____

_____

_____

_____

_____

What was a notable or "aha" moment from today,
and why?

_____

_____

_____

_____

_____

_____

_____

_____

_____

★

Day: _____ Date: ____ / ____ / ____

What are some ways that you feel "blessed" or
fortunate, and why?

_____

_____

_____

_____

_____

_____

_____

_____

_____

What was a notable or "aha" moment from today,
and why?

_____

_____

_____

_____

_____

_____

_____

_____

_____

★

Even on your worst day, it's important to realize that there is still so much right with your life.

Day: _____ Date: ___ / ___ / ___

How are you feeling right now,
and why?

_____

_____

_____

_____

_____

_____

_____

_____

_____

_____

What was a notable or "aha" moment from today,
and why?

_____

_____

_____

_____

_____

_____

_____

_____

_____

_____

★

Day: _____ Date: ____ / ____ / ____

*When was the last time you made caring for
yourself a priority? What did you do, and why?*

_____

_____

_____

_____

_____

_____

_____

_____

_____

*What was a notable or "aha" moment from today,
and why?*

_____

_____

_____

_____

_____

_____

_____

_____

★

Day: _____ Date: ____ / ____ / ____

What are a few of the more notable moments from the past week, and in what ways (if any) will this change how you approach things moving forward?

_____

_____

_____

_____

_____

_____

_____

_____

_____

_____

_____

_____

_____

_____

_____

_____

_____

_____

_____

★

Day: _____ Date: ____ / ____ / ____

If you knew you weren't going to be judged by
anyone, what would you do differently, and why?

_____

_____

_____

_____

_____

_____

_____

_____

_____

_____

What was a notable or "aha" moment from today,
and why?

_____

_____

_____

_____

_____

_____

_____

_____

_____

_____

★

Day: _____ Date: ____ / ____ / ____

*What was the last good (or bad) thing you did when
no one else was watching, and why did you do it?*

_____

_____

_____

_____

_____

_____

_____

_____

_____

*What was a notable or "aha" moment from today,
and why?*

_____

_____

_____

_____

_____

_____

_____

_____

_____

★

Day: _____ Date: ____ / ____ / ____

*How have you treated yourself with
value today?*

_____

_____

_____

_____

_____

_____

_____

_____

_____

_____

*What was a notable or "aha" moment from today,
and why?*

_____

_____

_____

_____

_____

_____

_____

_____

_____

★

Day: _____ Date: ____ / ____ / ____

*In what way did you respect (or disrespect) your
time today, and why?*

_____

_____

_____

_____

_____

_____

_____

_____

_____

_____

*What was a notable or "aha" moment from today,
and why?*

_____

_____

_____

_____

_____

_____

_____

_____

_____

_____

★

Day: _____ Date: ____ / ____ / ____

*When was the last time you said "yes" when you
really wanted to say "no," and why?*

_____

_____

_____

_____

_____

_____

_____

_____

_____

_____

*What was a notable or "aha" moment from today,
and why?*

_____

_____

_____

_____

_____

_____

_____

_____

_____

_____

★

Day: _____ Date: ___ / ___ / ___

What is the best conversation you've had so far this year? Who was it with, and what made it so memorable for you?

_____

_____

_____

_____

_____

_____

_____

_____

_____

_____

What was a notable or "aha" moment from today, and why?

_____

_____

_____

_____

_____

_____

_____

_____

_____

_____

★

Day: _____ Date: ____ / ____ / ____

What are a few of the more notable moments from the past week, and in what ways (if any) will this change how you approach things moving forward?

_____

_____

_____

_____

_____

_____

_____

_____

_____

_____

_____

_____

_____

_____

_____

_____

_____

_____

_____

Day: _____ Date: ____ / ____ / ____

When was the last time you felt accepted for who you are?

_____

_____

_____

_____

_____

_____

_____

_____

_____

What was a notable or "aha" moment from today, and why?

_____

_____

_____

_____

_____

_____

_____

_____

_____

★

Day: _____ Date: ____ / ____ / ____

*When was your last enjoyable moment? What
made it enjoyable?*

_____

_____

_____

_____

_____

_____

_____

_____

_____

_____

*What was a notable or "aha" moment from today,
and why?*

_____

_____

_____

_____

_____

_____

_____

_____

_____

_____

★

Day: _____ Date: ____ / ____ / ____

When was the last time you were stressed? What was going on, and how did you handle it?

_____

_____

_____

_____

_____

_____

_____

_____

_____

_____

What was a notable or "aha" moment from today, and why?

_____

_____

_____

_____

_____

_____

_____

_____

_____

_____

★

Day: _____ Date: ___ / ___ / ___

*What is something you've been really interested in
lately, and why?*

_____

_____

_____

_____

_____

_____

_____

_____

_____

*What was a notable or "aha" moment from today,
and why?*

_____

_____

_____

_____

_____

_____

_____

_____

_____

Day: _____ Date: ___ / ___ / ___

*What was your last mistake, and what did you
learn from it?*

_____

_____

_____

_____

_____

_____

_____

_____

_____

_____

*What was a notable or "aha" moment from today,
and why?*

_____

_____

_____

_____

_____

_____

_____

_____

_____

_____

✮

Day: _____ Date: ___ / ___ / ___

What do you normally worry about,
and why?

_____

_____

_____

_____

_____

_____

_____

_____

_____

What was a notable or "aha" moment from today,
and why?

_____

_____

_____

_____

_____

_____

_____

_____

_____

Day: _____ Date: ____ / ____ / ____

What are a few of the more notable moments from the past week, and in what ways (if any) will this change how you approach things moving forward?

_____

_____

_____

_____

_____

_____

_____

_____

_____

_____

_____

_____

_____

_____

_____

_____

_____

_____

_____

⭐

Day: _____ Date: ___ / ___ / ___

*What are two things you hope to achieve during
the coming month, and why?*

_____

_____

_____

_____

_____

_____

_____

_____

_____

_____

*What was a notable or "aha" moment from today,
and why?*

_____

_____

_____

_____

_____

_____

_____

_____

_____

★

Day: _____ Date: ____ / ____ / ____

*What is one positive habit you'd like to start
creating, and why?*

_____

_____

_____

_____

_____

_____

_____

_____

_____

*What was a notable or "aha" moment from today,
and why?*

_____

_____

_____

_____

_____

_____

_____

_____

_____

★

Day: _____ Date: ____ / ____ / ____

What was the last thing you bought,
and why?

_____

_____

_____

_____

_____

_____

_____

_____

_____

_____

What was a notable or "aha" moment from today,
and why?

_____

_____

_____

_____

_____

_____

_____

_____

_____

★

Day: _____ Date: ____ / ____ / ____

*How has your attitude been over the past week,
and why?*

_____

_____

_____

_____

_____

_____

_____

_____

_____

_____

*What was a notable or "aha" moment from today,
and why?*

_____

_____

_____

_____

_____

_____

_____

_____

_____

★

Day: _____ Date: ____ / ____ / ____

How has your mood been over the past week, and
why?

_____

_____

_____

_____

_____

_____

_____

_____

_____

_____

What was a notable or "aha" moment from today,
and why?

_____

_____

_____

_____

_____

_____

_____

_____

_____

_____

★

Day: _____ Date: ____ / ____ / ____

How has your relationship with money been over the past
month or year? Does anything need to change, and if so, what?

_____

_____

_____

_____

_____

_____

_____

_____

_____

_____

What was a notable or "aha" moment from today,
and why?

_____

_____

_____

_____

_____

_____

_____

_____

_____

★

Day:————————— Date:——— / ——— / ———

What are a few of the more notable moments from the past week, and in what ways (if any) will this change how you approach things moving forward?

_____

_____

_____

_____

_____

_____

_____

_____

_____

_____

_____

_____

_____

_____

_____

_____

_____

_____

_____

_____

Day: _____ Date: ____ / ____ / ____

*What are some ways you've been at war (or peace)
with yourself during the past week, and why?*

_____

_____

_____

_____

_____

_____

_____

_____

_____

_____

*What was a notable or "aha" moment from today,
and why?*

_____

_____

_____

_____

_____

_____

_____

_____

_____

★

Day: _____ Date: ____ / ____ / ____

What was the last creative thing you did, and what did you enjoy about it?

_____

_____

_____

_____

_____

_____

_____

_____

_____

What was a notable or "aha" moment from today, and why?

_____

_____

_____

_____

_____

_____

_____

_____

_____

★

Day: _____ Date: ___ / ___ / ___

*In what way has your inner strength been tested
this year, and why?*

_____

_____

_____

_____

_____

_____

_____

_____

_____

*What was a notable or "aha" moment from today,
and why?*

_____

_____

_____

_____

_____

_____

_____

_____

_____

★

Day: _____ Date: ____ / ____ / ____

If your life is your message to the world, then what message have you sent out over the past year, and why?

_____

_____

_____

_____

_____

_____

_____

_____

_____

_____

What was a notable or "aha" moment from today, and why?

_____

_____

_____

_____

_____

_____

_____

_____

_____

★

Day: _____ Date: ___ / ___ / ___

How are you feeling right now,
and why?

_____

_____

_____

_____

_____

_____

_____

_____

_____

_____

What was a notable or "aha" moment from today,
and why?

_____

_____

_____

_____

_____

_____

_____

_____

_____

★

Day: _____ Date: ____ / ____ / ____

*What is a deal breaker you have when it comes to
how people treat you, and why?*

_____

_____

_____

_____

_____

_____

_____

_____

_____

_____

*What was a notable or "aha" moment from today,
and why?*

_____

_____

_____

_____

_____

_____

_____

_____

_____

★

Having deal breakers when it comes to how others treat you isn't cruel—it is self-protective, and necessary.

Day:_____ Date:___ / ___ / ___

*What are a few of the more notable moments from the
past week, and in what ways (if any) will this change
how you approach things moving forward?*

_____

_____

_____

_____

_____

_____

_____

_____

_____

_____

_____

_____

_____

_____

_____

_____

_____

★

Day: _____ Date: ___ / ___ / ___

What are some of your greatest strengths, and why?

_____

_____

_____

_____

_____

_____

_____

_____

_____

_____

What was a notable or "aha" moment from today, and why?

_____

_____

_____

_____

_____

_____

_____

_____

_____

_____

★

Day: _____ Date: ____ / ____ / ____

What has really excited you lately,
and why?

_____

_____

_____

_____

_____

_____

_____

_____

_____

_____

What was a notable or "aha" moment from today,
and why?

_____

_____

_____

_____

_____

_____

_____

_____

_____

_____

✪

Day: _____ Date: ____ / ____ / ____

What is your favorite memory you've made so far
this year, and why?

_____

_____

_____

_____

_____

_____

_____

_____

_____

_____

What was a notable or "aha" moment from today,
and why?

_____

_____

_____

_____

_____

_____

_____

_____

_____

_____

★

Day: _____ Date: ____ / ____ / ____

If you had a mantra for this chapter of your life, what would it be, and why?

_____

_____

_____

_____

_____

_____

_____

_____

_____

What was a notable or "aha" moment from today, and why?

_____

_____

_____

_____

_____

_____

_____

_____

★

Day: _____ Date: ____ / ____ / ____

*What event(s) this year have been the most
transformative for you, and why?*

_____

_____

_____

_____

_____

_____

_____

_____

_____

_____

*What was a notable or "aha" moment from today,
and why?*

_____

_____

_____

_____

_____

_____

_____

_____

_____

_____

★

Day: _____ Date: ____ / ____ / ____

What was the last thing your intuition told you—
and did you listen? What was the outcome?

_____

_____

_____

_____

_____

_____

_____

_____

_____

_____

What was a notable or "aha" moment from today,
and why?

_____

_____

_____

_____

_____

_____

_____

_____

_____

★

Day: _____ Date: ____ / ____ / ____

What are a few of the more notable moments from the
past week, and in what ways (if any) will this change
how you approach things moving forward?

_____

_____

_____

_____

_____

_____

_____

_____

_____

_____

_____

_____

_____

_____

_____

_____

_____

_____

_____

★

Day: _____ Date: ____ / ____ / ____

Who has been the most influential person in your life this past year, and why?

_____

_____

_____

_____

_____

_____

_____

_____

What was a notable or "aha" moment from today, and why?

_____

_____

_____

_____

_____

_____

_____

_____

★

Day: _____ Date: ____ / ____ / ____

Who is someone you've really admired this year,
and why?

_____

_____

_____

_____

_____

_____

_____

_____

_____

_____

What was a notable or "aha" moment from today,
and why?

_____

_____

_____

_____

_____

_____

_____

_____

_____

★

Day: _____ Date: ____ / ____ / ____

What traits do you most appreciate about the last person you spent time with, and why?

_____

_____

_____

_____

_____

_____

_____

_____

_____

What was a notable or "aha" moment from today, and why?

_____

_____

_____

_____

_____

_____

_____

_____

_____

★

Day: _____ Date: ____ / ____ / ____

What was the last toxic relationship or situation you were in,
and why?

_____

_____

_____

_____

_____

_____

_____

_____

_____

_____

What was a notable or "aha" moment from today,
and why?

_____

_____

_____

_____

_____

_____

_____

_____

_____

_____

★

Day: _____ Date: ____ / ____ / ____

What is one area you feel stuck in, and what do
you think needs to happen for you to get unstuck?

_____

_____

_____

_____

_____

_____

_____

_____

_____

_____

What was a notable or "aha" moment from today,
and why?

_____

_____

_____

_____

_____

_____

_____

_____

_____

★

Day: _____ Date: ___ / ___ / ___

*What are two important criteria that others need
to meet to be part of your inner circle?*

_____

_____

_____

_____

_____

_____

_____

_____

_____

_____

*What was a notable or "aha" moment from today,
and why?*

_____

_____

_____

_____

_____

_____

_____

_____

_____

_____

✪

Day:_____ Date:____ / ____ / ____

What are a few of the more notable moments from the past week, and in what ways (if any) will this change how you approach things moving forward?

_____

_____

_____

_____

_____

_____

_____

_____

_____

_____

_____

_____

_____

_____

_____

_____

_____

_____

★

Day: _____ Date: ____ / ____ / ____

What is the last thing you criticized yourself for,
and why?

_____

_____

_____

_____

_____

_____

_____

_____

_____

_____

What was a notable or "aha" moment from today,
and why?

_____

_____

_____

_____

_____

_____

_____

_____

_____

_____

★

Day: _____ Date: ___ / ___ / ___

What does living a good life look like to you, and why?

_____

_____

_____

_____

_____

_____

_____

_____

_____

_____

What was a notable or "aha" moment from today, and why?

_____

_____

_____

_____

_____

_____

_____

_____

_____

_____

★

Day: _____ Date: ____ / ____ / ____

*What are two things you hope to achieve during
the coming month, and why?*

_____

_____

_____

_____

_____

_____

_____

_____

_____

*What was a notable or "aha" moment from today,
and why?*

_____

_____

_____

_____

_____

_____

_____

_____

_____

★

Day: _____ Date: ___ / ___ / ___

What is your favorite article of clothing,
and why?

_____

_____

_____

_____

_____

_____

_____

_____

_____

_____

What was a notable or "aha" moment from today,
and why?

_____

_____

_____

_____

_____

_____

_____

_____

_____

_____

★

Day: _____ Date: ____ / ____ / ____

What is something you do that keeps you feeling young, and why?

_____

_____

_____

_____

_____

_____

_____

_____

_____

_____

What was a notable or "aha" moment from today, and why?

_____

_____

_____

_____

_____

_____

_____

_____

_____

_____

★

Day: _____ Date: ____ / ____ / ____

What have you found relaxing lately? Why do you
think this is?

_____

_____

_____

_____

_____

_____

_____

_____

_____

_____

What was a notable or "aha" moment from today,
and why?

_____

_____

_____

_____

_____

_____

_____

_____

_____

_____

★

Day: _____ Date: ____ / ____ / ____

What are a few of the more notable moments from the
past week, and in what ways (if any) will this change
how you approach things moving forward?

_____

_____

_____

_____

_____

_____

_____

_____

_____

_____

_____

_____

_____

_____

_____

_____

_____

_____

_____

★

Day: _____ Date: ____ / ____ / ____

What has drained your energy lately,
and why?

_____

_____

_____

_____

_____

_____

_____

_____

_____

What was a notable or "aha" moment from today,
and why?

_____

_____

_____

_____

_____

_____

_____

_____

_____

★

Pay attention to the people, places, and things that either give you energy or drain you of energy. Invest your time wisely.

Day: _____ Date: ___ / ___ / ___

What has energized you lately,
and why?

_____

_____

_____

_____

_____

_____

_____

_____

_____

_____

What was a notable or "aha" moment from today,
and why?

_____

_____

_____

_____

_____

_____

_____

_____

_____

★

Day: _____ Date: ___ / ___ / ___

*What has been the most stressful situation you've been in this
year, and what about it was stressful?*

_____

_____

_____

_____

_____

_____

_____

_____

_____

*What was a notable or "aha" moment from today,
and why?*

_____

_____

_____

_____

_____

_____

_____

_____

_____

✯

It's pretty wild that we ever thought living a stressed-out life is somehow necessary or acceptable.

Day: _____ Date: ____ / ____ / ____

What was the last movie or TV show you watched,
and what did you like or dislike about it?

_____

_____

_____

_____

_____

_____

_____

_____

_____

_____

What was a notable or "aha" moment from today,
and why?

_____

_____

_____

_____

_____

_____

_____

_____

_____

_____

★

Day: _____ Date: ____ / ____ / ____

*What was the first thing you thought about when
you woke up this morning, and why?*

_____

_____

_____

_____

_____

_____

_____

_____

_____

_____

*What was a notable or "aha" moment from today,
and why?*

_____

_____

_____

_____

_____

_____

_____

_____

_____

★

Day: _____ Date: ____ / ____ / ____

What has been one of your biggest vulnerabilities
during the past year, and why do you think this is?

_____

_____

_____

_____

_____

_____

_____

_____

_____

_____

What was a notable or "aha" moment from today,
and why?

_____

_____

_____

_____

_____

_____

_____

_____

_____

_____

★

Day:_____ Date:____ / ____ / ____

What are a few of the more notable moments from the past week, and in what ways (if any) will this change how you approach things moving forward?

_____

_____

_____

_____

_____

_____

_____

_____

_____

_____

_____

_____

_____

_____

_____

_____

_____

_____

★

Day: _____ Date: ____ / ____ / ____

How did you cope with your last problem? Would you use the same technique to cope next time?

_____

_____

_____

_____

_____

_____

_____

_____

_____

What was a notable or "aha" moment from today, and why?

_____

_____

_____

_____

_____

_____

_____

_____

_____

_____

✮

Day: _____ Date: ____ / ____ / ____

What do you have a passionate belief about, and why?

_____

_____

_____

_____

_____

_____

_____

_____

_____

_____

What was a notable or "aha" moment from today, and why?

_____

_____

_____

_____

_____

_____

_____

_____

_____

★

Day: _____ Date: ____ / ____ / ____

What has been the most empowering belief that has moved you forward lately, and why?

_____

_____

_____

_____

_____

_____

_____

_____

_____

_____

What was a notable or "aha" moment from today, and why?

_____

_____

_____

_____

_____

_____

_____

_____

_____

_____

★

Day: _____ Date: ___ / ___ / ___

On a scale of 1-10 (one being low and ten being high),
how would you rate your self-esteem today, and why?

_____

_____

_____

_____

_____

_____

_____

_____

_____

What was a notable or "aha" moment from today,
and why?

_____

_____

_____

_____

_____

_____

_____

_____

_____

★

Day: _____ Date: ___ / ___ / ___

When was the last time you were negatively influenced by someone's opinion of you, and why?

_____

_____

_____

_____

_____

_____

_____

_____

_____

What was a notable or "aha" moment from today, and why?

_____

_____

_____

_____

_____

_____

_____

_____

_____

★

Day: _____ Date: ____ / ____ / ____

What are two ways you have treated yourself with respect during the past year?

_____

_____

_____

_____

_____

_____

_____

_____

_____

_____

What was a notable or "aha" moment from today, and why?

_____

_____

_____

_____

_____

_____

_____

_____

_____

_____

★

Any relationship or situation
that requires you to sacrifice
your dignity to be in, isn't worth
being in.

Day:_____ Date:____ /____ /____

What are a few of the more notable moments from the past week, and in what ways (if any) will this change how you approach things moving forward?

_____

_____

_____

_____

_____

_____

_____

_____

_____

_____

_____

_____

_____

_____

_____

_____

_____

_____

_____

_____

_____

★

Day: _____ Date: ____ / ____ / ____

How are you feeling right now,
and why?

_____

_____

_____

_____

_____

_____

_____

_____

_____

_____

What was a notable or "aha" moment from today,
and why?

_____

_____

_____

_____

_____

_____

_____

_____

_____

★

Day: _____ Date: ____ / ____ / ____

What is one quality you really like about yourself,
and why?

_____

_____

_____

_____

_____

_____

_____

_____

_____

_____

What was a notable or "aha" moment from today,
and why?

_____

_____

_____

_____

_____

_____

_____

_____

_____

_____

★

Day: _____ Date: ____ / ____ / ____

*What's been your favorite part of your day lately,
and why?*

_____

_____

_____

_____

_____

_____

_____

_____

_____

*What was a notable or "aha" moment from today,
and why?*

_____

_____

_____

_____

_____

_____

_____

_____

★

Day: _____ Date: ____ / ____ / ____

What is something you've done for the first time
lately? How did it go, and how did you feel about it?

_____

_____

_____

_____

_____

_____

_____

_____

_____

_____

What was a notable or "aha" moment from today,
and why?

_____

_____

_____

_____

_____

_____

_____

_____

_____

★

Day: _____ Date: ____ / ____ / ____

What have you overcome either in general, or during this past year,
that you previously didn't think you could conquer?

_____

_____

_____

_____

_____

_____

_____

_____

_____

_____

What was a notable or "aha" moment from today,
and why?

_____

_____

_____

_____

_____

_____

_____

_____

_____

_____

✮

Day: _____ Date: ___ / ___ / ___

What are one or two things you tend to take for
granted, and why?

_____

_____

_____

_____

_____

_____

_____

_____

_____

What was a notable or "aha" moment from today,
and why?

_____

_____

_____

_____

_____

_____

_____

_____

_____

★

Day: _____ Date: ____ / ____ / ____

What are a few of the more notable moments from the past week, and in what ways (if any) will this change how you approach things moving forward?

_____

_____

_____

_____

_____

_____

_____

_____

_____

_____

_____

_____

_____

_____

_____

_____

_____

_____

_____

★

Day: _____ Date: ____ / ____ / ____

What question(s) have you been trying to find an
answer to lately, and why?

_____

_____

_____

_____

_____

_____

_____

_____

_____

_____

What was a notable or "aha" moment from today,
and why?

_____

_____

_____

_____

_____

_____

_____

_____

_____

★

Day: _____ Date: ___ / ___ / ___

What was the last boundary you set with
someone? How did you feel about it?

_____

_____

_____

_____

_____

_____

_____

_____

_____

_____

What was a notable or "aha" moment from today,
and why?

_____

_____

_____

_____

_____

_____

_____

_____

_____

★

Day: _____ Date: ___ / ___ / ___

*What's been the best decision you've made lately,
and why?*

_____

_____

_____

_____

_____

_____

_____

_____

_____

*What was a notable or "aha" moment from today,
and why?*

_____

_____

_____

_____

_____

_____

_____

_____

_____

★

Day: _____ Date: ___ / ___ / ___

In what ways have you lived an authentic life
during the past month?

_____

_____

_____

_____

_____

_____

_____

_____

_____

What was a notable or "aha" moment from today,
and why?

_____

_____

_____

_____

_____

_____

_____

_____

_____

★

Day: _____ Date: ____ / ____ / ____

What two things are you dedicated to seeing
happen during the next year, and why?

_____

_____

_____

_____

_____

_____

_____

_____

_____

_____

What was a notable or "aha" moment from today,
and why?

_____

_____

_____

_____

_____

_____

_____

_____

_____

★

Dream big, and take small, consistent action in the direction you want to head.

Made in the USA
Las Vegas, NV
09 November 2021

34060313R00223